D1108223

om front f ⌐)

SPACE NOMADS

METEORITES IN SKY, FIELD, & LABORATORY

COURTESY OF AMERICAN MUSEUM OF NATURAL HISTORY

523.5
LAP

LINCOLN LAPAZ
AND JEAN LAPAZ

SPACE
NOMADS

METEORITES IN SKY,
FIELD, & LABORATORY

HOLIDAY HOUSE, NEW YORK

(frontispiece)
Fireball speeding across field of camera during the photographing of the Great Spiral Nebula in Andromeda, by Josef Klepesta, at the Prague Observatory, Czechoslovakia, September 12, 1923.

COPYRIGHT, 1961, BY LINCOLN LaPAZ & JEAN LaPAZ

PRINTED IN THE U.S.A.

PREFACE

M E T E O R I T I C S is the study of the only tangible entities that reach us from outer space. Except for the meteorites, scientists have to depend entirely on studies of some form of *radiation* for all their knowledge of the wider cosmos lying outside of the atmosphere of the earth. And none of the radiations reaching us from various sources afar can be held in the hand for examination. Each type of radiant energy incident upon our earth—whether that energy be light from the sun or from the more distant stars or the galaxies, or the reflected light from the planets and moons of our Solar System, or the less familiar forms of radiation, such as radio waves and cosmic rays—must be measured and permanently recorded by complicated instruments. Often the results given by even the most sensitive and tractable of these scientific robots turn out to be exceedingly difficult for man, their master, to interpret.

But the meteorites require no such temperamental instruments for their measurement. They are themselves a permanent record. They can be weighed, sectioned, and polished. They can be studied chemically, microscopically, and radiometrically. In fact, they can be investigated *directly,* just as they are themselves, in our hands, by any method modern science may be clever enough to devise.

This is why, now with the world's attention drawn to ambitious plans for the exploration of the cosmos, meteors and meteorites are of increasing interest and importance.

We have planned and written this book to be a sound and yet largely nontechnical introduction to the science of meteoritics. Our daily experiences in the Institute of Meteoritics have afforded us a fortunate advantage in making such a presentation. For, in addition to our work in the field, laboratory, and classrooms, we have frequently conducted young people through the museum and workrooms of the Institute and so have had the opportunity of learning their point of view at the same time they were venturing into ours. We hope our book will instill in the reader an abiding interest in the location and protection, the recovery and preservation and especially in the study of those cosmic missiles of iron, iron-stone, or stony composition that represent mankind's only ponderable links with the vast universe lying beyond the limits of the earth's atmosphere.

Although all photographs and special depictions not made by our staff are individually credited, we wish to express our personal thanks for the privilege of reprinting them here. All photographs that are without a credit line have been made by members of our staff.

Lincoln LaPaz   *Jean LaPaz*

University of New Mexico, Albuquerque, March 20, 1961

TABLE OF CONTENTS

SPACE NOMADS

METEORITES IN SKY, FIELD, & LABORATORY

Painting of the Ussuri fireball by the Iman artist, P. I. Medvedev.

1. A METEORITE FALLS IN THE TAIGA, U.S.S.R.

THE MORNING of February 12, 1947, dawned cold but bright and sunny in the wide Ussuri valley of Eastern Siberia. During the early morning hours the people in the villages went about their everyday chores as usual. Farmers fed and watered their livestock, while housewives tidied rooms and fired up stoves for heating and baking. Miners went to work deep underground. An artist seated himself outdoors near his home to make exercise sketches. In a densely wooded area on the slopes of a nearby mountain range, a logging crew began a day's timber-cutting.

Suddenly, at 10:35 a.m., an extraordinarily large and brilliant fireball flashed above the central part of the mountain range. It streaked across the sky in less than 5 seconds and disappeared beyond the western foothills of the range. Then the inhabitants of a wide area heard what seemed to them a mighty thunderclap followed by a powerful roar like an artillery cannonade. Many people felt a strong airwave. (Field parties later found that those who noticed this effect were quite close to the place where the meteorite fell.)

For several hours afterward, a large black column of smoke tinged with a reddish-rose color stood above the place of fall. Gradually, this cloud spread outward, became curved and then zigzag in form, and finally vanished toward the end of the day.

The flash of the fireball and the loud noises that followed it caused panic among the farm animals. Cows lowed mournfully and herds of goats scattered in every direction, chickens and other fowl squawked in alarm, and dogs ran whining for shelter or crouched against the legs of their masters.

In the villages, the airwave blew snow off the roofs of houses and other buildings, while the strong earth-shocks opened windows and made doors swing ajar. Housewives were dismayed to see glass windowpanes shattered in their frames and burning coals and firebrands jolted out of the wood-burning stoves.

Even deep in the mineshaft, the vibrations in the air were strong enough to snuff out the miners' lamps, leaving the men in darkness.

On seeing the huge fireball streak across the sky, the artist put aside his practice sketch and began a picture of the display before his impressions of it could fade. His painting of this natural event is now famous. Not only is it on display in scientific museums all around the world, but a color reproduction of it has been issued in Russia as a postage stamp.

The forester supervising the logging crew reported that his attention was first attracted to the sky when he noticed a strange "second" shadow rotating rapidly about the tree that cast it. On looking up, he saw a blindingly bright fireball, twice as large as the sun, a fiery globe that threw off multicolored sparks as it passed. Not long after the fireball disappeared behind the trees, the forester heard a loud noise like nearby cannonading and saw a large dark-colored cloud—later tinged with red— billow up over the impact point. (The members of the logging crew were among the very few persons actually abroad near the place of fall. It turned out that they were only about 9 miles from it.)

As soon as the many eyewitnesses of the fireball had recovered from their fright, the questions almost everyone asked were "What could it have been?" and "Where did it come down?" To answer the first question was not as difficult as to answer the second. Local scientists in Vladivostok and Khabarovsk, the nearest cities of some size, suspected from the first that a very large meteorite fall had occurred. But exactly where? All they could be certain of was that the impact point lay in the Ussuri taiga, a formidable wilderness.

The Sikhote-Alin mountains lie along the Siberian coast between the Sea of Japan and the Tatar Strait. The Ussuri taiga is a vast, low-lying, marshy, densely forested region fronting the western flanks of these mountains. Ordinary cedars, pines, oaks, and aspen grow in the taiga, but the region is also noted for such rare plants and trees as the celebrated ginseng, the cork tree, the Greek nut tree, and the black birch. Wild grape and ivy vines intertwine the upper branches of the thick forest, and the trunks of the trees themselves rise from an almost impenetrable maze of brush and downed timber.

So dense is the forest that in summer, a man can see no more than 10 or 12 feet in any direction. Yet in winter, the explorer's lot is no easier; for, although the deciduous trees then stand leafless, the ground is covered by three feet or more of snow. And in the early fall, violent cloudbursts often flood the taiga, making travel impossible.

Such was the inhospitable region in which the Ussuri, or (as it is now known in the U.S.S.R.) Sikhote-Alin meteorite, had chanced to fall. For any search parties traveling on the ground, the likelihood that they could find the fallen meteorite in that wilderness would have been very small.

The impact point of the Ussuri meteorite was discovered in the only way really practical: from the air. Fortunately, the center of impact lay almost directly below the airlane connecting the towns of Iman and Ulunga, so that the devastation produced by the meteorite fall in the taiga was clearly visible to aviators following this active air route.

The accounts several fliers gave concerning the widespread cratering and destruction they had seen from the air in the impact area led to the organization of two separate ground-search parties, one at Khabarovsk, the other at Vladivostok. The Khabarovsk group, made up of four members of the Geological Society, flew to the village of Kharkovo, the inhabited point nearest the site of fall. After a rough and dangerous landing on the small, snow-covered airfield at Kharkovo, the geologists began their trek into the taiga on foot. Throughout the entire trip, the men, burdened with supplies and equipment, waded through waist-deep snow and camped in the open despite the arctic cold.

At almost the same time, a geologist from Vladivostok set out from the railway line up the Ussuri valley to track down the fallen meteorite. His progress was even more difficult than that of the Khabarovsk party. In addition to following a much longer route, he did not have the invaluable information that the first party had got from the aviators. He had to make his

COURTESY OF E. L. KRINOV

Splintered and broken trees at the site of the Ussuri fall.

way slowly from village to village, questioning eyewitnesses as he went and gradually determining the probable end-point of the meteorite fall.

The route followed by the Vladivostok geologist lay through the heart of the trackless snow-covered taiga. Fortunately, he had with him two hunters who were well acquainted with the rigors of travel through the taiga and knew how to live off the land.

They slept in hunters' huts or under overhanging trees, drank melted snow water, and ate fried quail. But they had not gone far when they found that their footwear was completely useless for a trek through the wet, snowy taiga, because their felt hiking boots quickly soaked up water and became very heavy. So they swathed their feet in warm dry grass over which they tied large pieces of untanned leather. After that, the walking was much easier. They were able to cover the ground so rapidly that they reached Kharkovo only a day after the Khabarovsk geologists had landed there at the small airfield.

At Kharkovo, the three feasted on pork, milk, and honey. Then loading a few provisions on a borrowed horse, they started out to overtake the Khabarovsk party. They made such good time that the two groups were able to join forces and to enter the impact area as one expedition, on February 24, 1947.

A scene of great desolation awaited them in the central region of the meteorite fall. Masses of crushed stone had been hurled hundreds of feet by the violent impact. Denuded, up-rooted trees lay about—some cut in two as neatly as if by a saw. Large cedars had been splintered where they stood or had

COURTESY OF E. L. KRINOV

Workmen excavating one of the large craters formed by the impact of the Ussuri meteorites.

been torn up by the roots and thrown some scores of yards.

Most impressive of all, though, were the numerous meteorite craters ranging in size from small bowl-like features to a basin more than 28 yards across and over 6 yards deep—a depression large enough to hold a two-story house. The investigators recovered many fragments of the iron meteorite that had broken to pieces not far above the earth's surface and had peppered the area of fall with high-speed meteoritic "shrapnel."

With their meteorite recoveries and photographs of the cratered area, the members of this first expedition returned to their respective towns and began a campaign by letter and wire to interest the Moscow office of the Academy of Sciences of the U.S.S.R. in making a full-scale investigation of the Ussuri fall. The officials of the Academy decided at once to send a special scientific expedition to the site of the meteorite fall.

A member of this later and better-equipped expedition compared the Ussuri crater field to a bombed-out area. In fact, some of the meteorite specimens were fragments that closely resembled pieces of shattered shell-casing. The edges of these fragments were jagged and bent, and their surfaces, which often displayed a rainbow-colored sheen, were grooved and scarred by impact against the hard rock underlying the region in which the crater field had been formed. In rare instances, the investigators noted spiral twisting of the fragments, an indication of the unusually violent disruptive forces to which they had been subjected at impact.

The scientists found several instances in which fist-sized meteorite fragments had actually penetrated into or through

COURTESY OF E. L. KRINOV

A nickel-iron meteorite from the Ussuri fall imbedded in the trunk of a cedar tree.

standing tree trunks, either becoming imbedded in the wood or driving a hole right through the trunk.

Many whole individual meteorites also were recovered. These were almost always covered by a thin, smooth "glaze" known as *fusion crust*. This crust forms on the surface of a meteorite as it plunges rapidly through the air. The heat generated during its flight causes the outer "skin" of the meteorite to melt. Later, when the mass has cooled off, the thin coating of melted material hardens, forming a rind or crust.

By the beginning of 1951, the Russians had sent three more expeditions to the site of the Ussuri fall. Their scientists found, in all, 122 craters (the largest more than 80 feet in diameter) as well as numerous funnels resulting from the penetration of smaller meteorites into the earth. By means of both visual and instrumental searches, they also recovered 20,000 meteoritic fragments and individual meteorites. The smallest Ussuri specimens weighed no more than the thousandth part of a gram. (There are 453.59 grams in a pound.) Some of these tiny masses were found lying cupped in leaves. The largest individual meteorite recovered weighed about 3,839 pounds. Altogether, approximately 23 tons of meteoritic material from the Ussuri fall are now in the collection of the Meteorite Committee of the Academy of Sciences, Moscow, while another 47 tons are believed to still be buried in the Ussuri crater field.

The Russian scientists carefully mapped the locations of the individual craters, penetration funnels, and meteorite recoveries. They made geologic and magnetometric surveys of the crater field, took aerial photographs of the entire area of fall,

COURTESY OF E. L. KRINOV

An individual Ussuri meteorite with fusion crust and characteristic surface sculpturing produced during high-speed flight through the resisting atmosphere.

and prepared a documentary motion-picture covering the activities of the various expeditions. The area of the crater field has been set aside by the Russian government as a sort of scientific preserve, and is being made into the equivalent of what is termed a National Monument in the U.S.A. Several of the typical craters are protected by overroofed shelters to preserve these features for generations yet to come.

2. A METEORITE FALLS IN THE WHEATLAND, U.S.A.

FEBRUARY 18, 1948, had been a pleasant day in northwestern Kansas and as the supper hour approached, the sky remained blue and cloudless. Shortly before 5:00 p.m., a few people were still out of doors. An eleven-year old girl was hanging up the last of the family wash on a high clothesline. In the late afternoon sunshine, a woman and her son were enjoying a walk around the back yard of their home on a large Kansas ranch. Outside his house, a ten-year old boy was playing basketball with friends. A veteran of World War II was loading fodder in a silo. In the feedlot of his ranch, a farmer was stacking hay. A filling station attendant was working outside at the pumps, grateful for a spell of milder winter weather.

Without warning, a large and very bright fireball streaked across the clear sky from southwest to northeast. Ominous-looking white smoke-clouds mushroomed up from points in the fireball's path. Shortly after the fireball disappeared, loud explosions and rumbling sounds drove thousands of people out into the open. The whole astonishing luminous display was over in a few seconds, but the strange clouds and the frightening sounds that followed the fireball's passage continued much longer.

Although startled by the brilliant fireball and the strange thundering noises, the young girl, whose face had been turned skyward as she hung up the clothes, noted very carefully where she had seen the fireball disappear behind the tallest building in her home town. (Her sighting was later of great value to field parties from the Institute of Meteoritics of the University of New Mexico.)

The woman and her son were amazed to see an angry, boiling white cloud tinged with red developing overhead in the blue sky and to hear strange whizzing noises in the air around them.

The boy playing basketball heard a peculiar whistling or hissing noise just as he was ready to shoot a basket and, on looking up, saw the ball of fire slanting earthward. (This boy's report was of particular interest, since it related to an unusual type of "sound" that travels at the speed of light rather than at the velocity of ordinary soundwaves.)

As a cannonading louder than any the veteran had heard on the battlefields of Europe echoed over the rolling countryside, he went temporarily into a state of shock.

The farmer stacking hay heard several explosions, felt a violent air blast, and finally heard a solid object strike the ground "with a smack," as he put it, "like a clod hitting the earth." (Later, field searchers found that this man lived only about two and a half miles south of the point where the largest fragment of the meteorite fell.)

Shortly after the passage of the fireball, the filling station attendant felt the legs of his trousers flap as if he were standing in a high wind, although he was more than 11 miles distant from the actual path along which the fireball moved on its way to the earth.

As in the case of the Ussuri fall, which had occurred about a year earlier, farm animals, chickens, and dogs were terrified by the strange and noisy event. Cattle tried to run through a fence to escape the deafening racket. A fine pair of horses panicked and ran headlong into a narrow gully, the walls of which collapsed on them during their struggles. Chickens dashed for the henhouse, screeching and cackling all the way. A dog that feared lightning jumped behind a haystack and finally ran to his master in alarm.

Although the majority of the people did not see the fireball itself, they were driven out-of-doors by the violent concussions that followed its passage, and thus got out under the open sky in ample time to see several large, turbulent white clouds mushrooming far overhead. From these clouds, a thick powder or dust filtered down through the air and collected on the surfaces of stock ponds and water tanks.

Some people thought the peculiar clouds were similar to those produced by atom bomb explosions. Many suspected that a V-2 rocket had "run away" from the proving ground at White Sands, New Mexico. One man disagreed with the opinion of his friends that the military had been experimenting and declared that it was "the Lord who was experimenting!"

The February 18 meteorite fall caused great excitement throughout Kansas and Nebraska, and it was the chief topic of conversation for days among the residents of the many small farming communities along the western half of the Kansas-Nebraska state line.

The Ussuri fall was studied by Russian scientists exclusively, and we have of necessity given, in Chapter 1, a secondhand account of the fall and surveys the Russians made; but field parties from the Institute of Meteoritics conducted on-the-spot investigations of the Norton, Kansas fall. As we were members of several of these field parties, the story to follow is a firsthand report.

A little before 6:00 p.m. on February 18, word of the mysterious explosion centering near Norton, Kansas reached the Institute of Meteoritics, in Albuquerque, N. M., through the kind offices of Civil Air Patrol personnel. Since a number of early reports had described the incident as an airplane falling in flames, it was only natural that the Civil Air Patrol and similar groups would take an interest in the occurrence. At once, the staff of the Institute began to interview eyewitnesses of the event through Civil Air Patrol channels and by long distance telephone, telegram, and letter. Soon we had collected enough information to show clearly that a large meteorite fall had been responsible for the unusual light and sound effects that had startled the inhabitants of Kansas, Nebraska, and adjoining states.

By March 3, the Institute staff had made a first determination of the probable area of fall. The center of this oval-shaped, 8 by 4 mile area lay about 15 miles north-northwest of Norton, Kansas and nearly on the Kansas-Nebraska state line. The meteorite had fallen in a region of wheat fields, pasture lands, and widely scattered farm houses. The countryside there is open and gently rolling. The small creeks winding through shallow valleys are marked in spring and summer by narrow bands of

A fragment of the Norton fall is removed still imbedded in the tough
buffalo grass sod into which it penetrated.

low green trees and bushes. Many of the hillsides are covered with unplowed buffalo sod.

On March 24, a field party left the University of New Mexico to make a survey of this area. Unfortunately, Kansas blizzards can be as severe as any in Siberia, and although the scientists gathered many helpful reports from eyewitnesses of the fall, heavy snow and high winds seriously hampered the work. The information they collected, however, confirmed the accuracy of the Institute staff's first determination of the probable area of fall.

Late in the spring, a farmer in this area found a "strange stone" on his land and held it for identification by the second Institute party. This strange stone—which smelled like sulfur and had metallic specks in it—was the first piece of the fallen meteorite to be recovered.

Scientists and farmers soon found many other fragments during systematic searches of the rolling farm and pasture lands. The fourteen-year-old boy who had been walking with his mother at the time of the fall discovered a 130-pound fragment of the meteorite in a pasture that had already been carefully searched by grown-up meteorite hunters! This find was one of the two largest fragments recovered from the entire fall. The landing place of this large piece was marked only by a small hole in the sod, but, on prodding into this hole, the boy struck something rather solid. He ran at once to tell the lady who owned the pastureland, and together they dug out the fine meteorite.

This discovery brought interest in finding meteorites to a

The Furnas County, Nebraska, stony meteorite in place at the bottom of its 10-foot "penetration funnel."

fever pitch, and it was soon possible to look in almost any direction and see farmers, or their wives and children, walking slowly across the fields and looking for meteorites.

Finally, in August, two farmers cutting wheat in a field just a short distance north of the Kansas-Nebraska state line found a deep hole when their tractor almost fell into it. They investigated and discovered that a very large fragment of the meteorite had buried itself deep in the ground.

Scientists from the University of Nebraska and the Institute of Meteoritics carefully excavated this huge meteorite. They found that the mass had plunged more than 10 feet into the earth. Quite by chance, its lower surface had come to rest in the ashes of a long-buried primitive cooking site.

The excavated meteorite looked and felt like a huge stone. Actually, it was stony in nature, but of a texture so fragile that it had to be wrapped in tissue paper, then in burlap, and finally covered with a thick coating of plaster of Paris before it could be lifted out of the ground. Those in charge of the removal of the meteorite borrowed this procedure from the paleontologists, who use it in the removal of fossil tusks and bones that otherwise would crumble away.

After the great meteorite had been raised out of the excavation, it was taken by truck to the University of New Mexico, in Albuquerque. There it was put on display beside the smaller 130-pound fragment found in May. By careful measurements, scientists determined the weight of the main mass to be approximately 2,360 pounds—a record weight for stony meteorites.*

* Also called *aerolites*.

Field party proudly surrounds the Furnas stone in its protective "armor."

This remarkable meteorite, known as the Furnas County, Nebraska, stone, is now a prized item in the collection of the Institute of Meteoritics.

As more and more finds were made in the area of fall, we accurately recorded their weights and mapped their locations. In this way, we could tell how the pieces of the meteorite had distributed themselves according to size and weight over the oval-shaped area. The smaller and lighter fragments were slowed down by air resistance and fell first, while the 2,360-pound mass carried on beyond them and came to earth at the farthest point along the direction of flight.

The staff of the Institute took many photographs of the meteorites that were found, of the impact funnel made by the largest mass, and of the excavation and removal of that giant stone. Some of these pictures were published in scientific journals, others in magazine and newspaper articles. A few of our best photographs are included in this chapter.

Although the light and sound effects that accompanied the Ussuri and Norton falls were similar, the meteorites recovered from them were not at all alike. The Ussuri specimens were masses of nickel-iron so malleable that on high-speed impact with hard rock they had held together and taken twisted and ragged shapes. But the Norton meteorites were very fragile stony masses, many of which went to pieces either in the air or when they struck the ground. Almost all of the recoveries made of this very rare type of stony meteorite were fragments, not whole specimens. They somewhat resembled pieces of a strange whitish mixture of chalk and crystalline limestone containing

The Furnas stone, protected by its "armor," hangs suspended from the truck crane that raised it out of its deep "penetration funnel" in the earth.

tiny specks and lumps of nickel-iron. Many specimens were covered wholly or in part by a shiny varnish-like fusion crust, varying in color from jet black through yellow to almost pure white.

The largest meteorite recovered from the Norton fall was the 2,360-pound mass that formed the deep impact funnel. The smallest Norton specimens, like their Ussuri counterparts, weighed no more than the thousandth part of a gram. Altogether, nearly a ton and a half of meteoritic material from the Norton fall was collected by the Institute. Other small fragments may remain undiscovered in the Kansas and Nebraska wheatlands, but, unfortunately, because of the soft and fragile nature of the material they are composed of, it is likely that they have now weathered away so completely that they are no longer recognizable as meteorites.

Our stories of the Ussuri and Norton meteorite falls show how hard scientists work themselves (and others!) to find meteorites. Therefore meteorites must be important. The two accounts given also make clear that investigators of meteorite falls are almost entirely dependent upon observations made by nonscientists.

Scientists investigating meteorite falls greatly appreciate the help given them by children and adults alike. Field parties are powerless without it, and we should like to encourage people of all ages to continue this type of valuable cooperation. In Chapter 7, we shall tell more about how the individual observer of a meteorite fall can make his report really count.

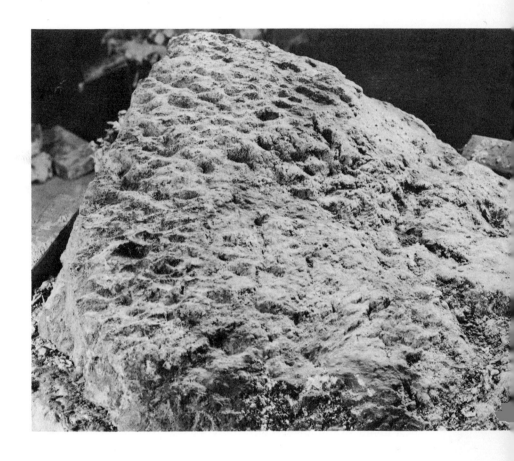

A close-up of the Furnas County stone, the largest stony meteorite
ever recovered.

3. FOUND AND LOST GIANTS

ALL METEORITES ARE important from the standpoint of science, but a few deserve special mention because of the human-interest stories connected with them.

First place among famous finds should no doubt go to the massive Cape York, Greenland, iron, the largest recovered meteorite actually to have been weighed. The Eskimos called this enormous object "Ahnighito," which means "The Tent." Robert E. Peary, the discoverer of the North Pole, brought it to New York City by ship in 1897. His party had great difficulty hoisting the 34-ton mass aboard. Later, when the ship had put to sea, she encountered a serious navigational hazard. To the amazement and alarm of the crew, the huge nickel-iron meteorite caused magnetic disturbances that severely affected the ship's compass.

Another of the giant meteorites, the 14-ton Willamette, Oregon, iron, became the center of a long legal battle in the early 1900's. The man who originally found the meteorite and recognized its true nature felt that because the iron was on the surface of the ground and not buried beneath it (as the ore of a metal would have been), there was no reason why he should not move the mass from the place of find to his own property, three-fourths of a mile away. He did this very laboriously by means of a log-timber car, a capstan with wire rope, and a small horse. On learning what the finder had done, the company that owned the land from which the meteorite had been removed put its attorneys on the job of recovering the "purloined"

COURTESY OF AMERICAN MUSEUM OF NATURAL HISTORY

Peary's photograph of the Cape York meteorite as it was being moved for loading aboard his ship. Arrival of the 34-ton iron mass at the American Museum of Natural History, New York City.

meteorite. The Oregon courts, bowing to decisions made in previous cases involving ownership of meteorites, brought in a verdict favoring the owners of the land. Although the finder of the Willamette meteorite lost the decision, he nevertheless won the distinction of being the only man to have successfully made off with a treasure weighing 14 tons!

The biggest meteorite of all, of course, is the one that "got away." In 1916, a captain in the Mauritanian army was taken by a native guide, secretly and at night, to the site of a colossal iron meteorite located in the dunes of the Adrar desert, in the far western reaches of the vast Sahara. The officer described the mass as measuring 100 meters (over 300 feet) by 40 meters (over 120 feet), with the third dimension hidden by the sand dunes. According to him, the mass "... jutted up in the midst of sand dunes that were covered by a desert plant, the *sba*, and it had the form of a compact, unfissured parallelopiped. The visible portion of the surface was vertical, dominating in the manner of a cliff, the wind-blown sand that was scooped away from the base of the mass so that the summit overhung; and that portion exposed to eolian [wind] erosion was polished like a mirror."

The captain, at the request of his uneasy guide, returned from his hurried excursion without taking notes or making a map. But he did bring back a small 10-pound fragment of iron which he had found lying on top of the giant mass. This small fragment later proved to be a genuine meteorite, and is the only known specimen of the famous Adrar mass. It is preserved at present in the Museum of Natural History at Paris.

What has been called a conspiracy of silence among the na-

J. OTIS WHEELOCK PHOTO
COURTESY OF AMERICAN MUSEUM OF NATURAL HISTORY

Man and boy carrying off the famous "purloined" Willamette meteorite on a homemade dolly car with wheels of tree-trunk sections.
Note hole piercing this 14-ton chunk of iron.

tives of the Adrar area and the inhospitable nature of the region itself have successfully preserved the secret of the location of the enormous metallic mass described by the captain. The native guide died, apparently of poison, and although many inhabitants of the region are no doubt familiar with the whereabouts of the mass (whatever it is!), those questioned have consistently denied knowledge of its very existence. All recent attempts, not only by military but even by scientific expeditions, to relocate the gigantic metallic mass have failed. The whole Adrar case remains an intriguing puzzle to be unraveled, it is hoped, by future generations of meteorite hunters.

Another "lost" meteorite is one composed of stone and iron. The Port Orford, Oregon, stony-iron (as it is now named) was originally found in 1859 by a U.S. geologist who was engaged in a survey of what were then the Oregon and Washington Territories. According to him, the mass was quite irregular in shape and "4 or 5 feet [of it] projected from the surface of the mountain," while it was "about the same number of feet in width and perhaps 3 or 4 feet in thickness." He broke off a small fragment of it (far smaller than the one taken from Adrar) and packed this specimen away with his collection of rock and mineral samples. Years later, the geological collection was cataloged and analyzed in the East. At that time, the fragment collected in 1859 was found to be a piece of a stony-iron meteorite. After that, scientists and others made many attempts to rediscover the main mass of the large Port Orford meteorite, all of them unsuccessful. Today the sum total of material recovered from this stony-iron amounts to 25 grams in the U.S. National

Museum, about 4 grams in the Natural History Museum of Vienna, and a few tiny specks in the Museum of the Geological Survey of India.

The Red River, Texas, iron is still another famous meteorite. It was originally discovered by Pawnee and Hietan Indians, and a group of them took a party of traders, in 1808, to the site. Two years later, two rival parties, each led by a man who had been a member of the 1808 trading expedition, began a search for the meteorite. The members of one of the two parties were from Nacogodoches, Texas. They reached the meteorite first but had left home so hurriedly on their eager hunt that they were not properly prepared to move so large a mass. They went away from the site to get horses and a wagon, after they had laboriously hidden the meteorite under a huge flat stone, to prevent the other party from finding it. The members of the other party, hailing from Natchitoches, Louisiana, set out better prepared. After a lengthy hunt, they finally found the hidden meteorite. Using tools they had the foresight to bring, they built a truck wagon and drove away with their prize. Eventually, the Red River meteorite, weighing 1,635 pounds, became a part of the collection at Yale University. But two other, smaller, masses of the same metal, known in the early days to the Pawnees and a few traders, remain still undiscovered in the Red River area.

4. WHEN IS A CRATER A METEORITE CRATER?

NOT ALL meteorites form craters at impact, as the larger Ussuri fragments did. Even the largest mass of the Norton meteorite merely buried itself in a funnel-like hole only about 10 feet deep. And the Russian investigators found a number of the lighter Ussuri fragments at the bottom of small penetration funnels. Cosmic missiles that are large enough to blast out craters in the ground are of particular interest to science, however, not only because of the extraordinarily intense light, sound, and other effects that accompany their fall, but also because they produce characteristic and long-lasting basin-like features in the outer shell of the earth.

Natural processes that change the surface features of the earth have long been the subjects of field studies by scientists. Geologists have carefully investigated the major folds formed in the earth's crust by mountain-building forces, the clefts and depressions resulting from earthquake activity and erosion, and the vast plains leveled off by the scouring action of great ice-sheets. All of these different natural processes, though, have one thing in common: their source is the earth-body itself. They take place either *within* the earth's crust as a result of local shifts or changes in pressure (like earthquakes and volcanic eruptions), or *on* the surface of the earth as a result of the action of water or of changes in temperature (like erosion and glaciation).

On the other hand, meteorite impact craters are not formed

by earth-processes at all. As we have seen, they result when large bodies of matter from the regions of space *outside* the earth chance to strike the surface of our planet at high speed. The study of meteorite craters is therefore a special field. It is also one of quite recent development; not until 1905 was the first meteorite crater recognized as such.

The first thing to be said on this subject is, of course, that not all holes in the ground, however large and impressive, were necessarily formed by the impact of meteorites. Features that resemble meteorite craters may result from certain ordinary earth-processes. For example, the rock layers underlying a particular area may be dissolved away by waters circulating beneath the surface of the ground. The overlying crust will eventually collapse into the empty space, and what geologists call a "sink hole" or a "sink" is formed. Many such sinks surround the genuine meteorite crater near Odessa, Texas, and at times have been mistaken for the real thing.

Since there is some possibility of confusion about whether or not a hole in the ground is a meteorite crater, it is comforting to know that scientists have come up with a handy set of rules for reaching a decision on this point. These rules can be stated in the form of several questions that crater-investigators should ask themselves:

Have you found meteorites in or near the crater-like feature?

In its vicinity, have you found pieces of country rock that show the effects of high temperature and pressure (melting or crushing)?

Did people actually see a meteorite come to earth at the point where the crater is located and where, to their certain knowledge, no crater existed before?

If the answer to all—or even one—of these questions is yes, then it is quite likely that the crater-like feature is actually a meteorite crater. Naturally, if the answer to the *first* question is yes, the matter is practically settled in favor of the meteoritic origin of the feature.

If the impact has taken place in horizontally bedded rock strata—that is, in flat beds of rock lying one on top of another like the layers in a stack of griddle cakes—a meteorite crater will have a characteristic *rim* of upturned or even overturned rock layers. (None of the ordinary sink holes near the Odessa crater show such rims.) In addition, pieces of rock shattered and thrown out by the impact will be found in all directions around the crater. The amount and size of this fragmented material will decrease with distance outward from the crater.

A list of the recognized (or genuine) meteorite craters of the world is given in the table on page 65. All of these craters except the two Russian ones were formed many thousands of years ago, and, in most cases, the earth processes of erosion and weathering have by now dimmed the sharp outlines of their rims and silted up their deep interior funnels until only basin-like bowls remain.

You may have visited the very first crater in the world to be recognized by scientists as a meteorite crater. This huge basin, now known as the Canyon Diablo meteorite crater (although

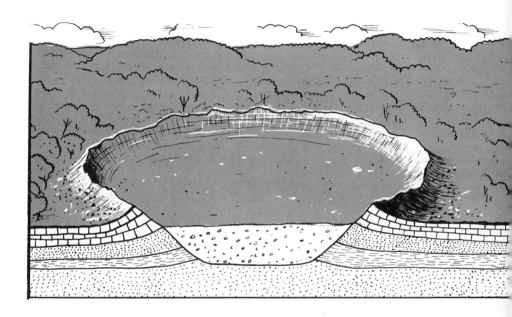

Cross-section showing the manner in which horizontally bedded rock strata may be broken and tilted upward by the impact of a crater-forming meteorite. This schematic diagram is based on excavations at several meteorite craters.

often referred to incorrectly as "Meteor Crater"), lies about 20 miles west of Winslow, Arizona. It is the best known of all the craters listed in the table because in recent years it has been developed under private ownership as one of the leading tourist attractions on U.S. Highway 66.

From the paved road that turns off Highway 66 toward the crater, the visitor sees the rim as a chain of low, hummocky, tan-colored hills which contrast sharply with the grayish or reddish hue of the desert plain.

The outer slopes of the crater rim rise very gently from the level plain in which the crater was formed, and they are covered with rock fragments of various sizes thrown out at the time the meteorite struck the earth. This fragmented material ranges in size from tiny particles of "rock-flour" as soft as face-powder to gigantic solid masses like Monument Rock, which is estimated to weigh 4,000 tons.

Field parties have found 50- to 100-pound fragments of the limestone layer underlying the Canyon Diablo area at distances of 1½ to 2 miles from the crater. Sizable rock and meteorite fragments out to distances of 6 miles from the rim have turned up, and smaller fragments of both materials at even greater distances.

On their first visit to the Canyon Diablo crater, people are always astonished at the steepness of the inner walls of the crater and at the very great size of its bowl. This crater is more than 4,000 feet across and 570 feet deep. It is the largest *recognized* meteorite crater so far discovered in the world, although other larger, basin-like features elsewhere on the surface of the

COURTESY OF TRANS-WORLD AIRLINES

Aerial view of the Canyon Diablo, Arizona, meteorite crater.

earth have been suspected but not proved to have a similar origin.

When the Canyon Diablo meteorite plunged into the horizontally bedded rock layers underlying the area of fall, the force of the explosion following the impact actually bent these layers upward. All around the inside of the crater, the rock strata tilt away from the center at steep angles.

Cowboys, ranchers, and scientists have found thousands of solid nickel-iron meteorite fragments around the crater. The largest of these weighs 1,406 pounds. The smallest spherules and grains are almost or quite microscopic in size. (These tiny granules have been well known to scientists since 1905 in spite of current fables claiming that they are a recent discovery.) In the rim and on the plain outside the crater, large and small *shale balls,* composed of weathered meteoritic material, were found in considerable numbers in the early days. Along with many solid iron meteorites, shale balls have also been found at various depths in recent times by field parties from the Institute employing specially designed meteorite detectors.

In the first two decades of the twentieth century, investigators sank (at great expense!) a number of shafts and drill holes in the interior and on the south rim of the crater, in unsuccessful attempts to locate the supposed "main mass" of the Canyon Diablo meteorite. Most authorities now believe, however, that the extremely high temperatures, developed at the time the Canyon Diablo meteorite penetrated into the earth, changed almost all of the gigantic cosmic missile into vapor.

No better example of an ancient meteorite crater has been

View of the interior of the Canyon Diablo crater showing the steep inner slopes of the huge basin.

Oceanside Public Library

found than this one near Canyon Diablo. The other craters listed in the table (even the two recently formed ones), while bearing resemblances to it, also show individual differences from it.

Some, like Henbury, Campo del Cielo, and Haviland, are not single craters but rather consist of fields of craters. In these cases, the earth was struck not by a single large meteoritic body that held together right down to impact, but either by a "swarm" of meteorites traveling together through space or by the fragments of a large meteorite that separated into pieces shortly before it struck the surface of the ground.

Again, the type of ground into which the meteorite strikes affects the character of the craters formed. As an illustration, the Wabar, Arabia, craters were not smashed out of sedimentary, horizontally bedded rock layers (as was the Canyon Diablo crater) but were formed in clean desert sand dunes. In this case, the crater rims are composed primarily of almost pure silica-glass formed by the fusion of the sand at the time of impact. It is not hard to imagine the terrific boiling and frothing up of melted sand and meteoritic material that must have accompanied the formation of the Wabar craters.

Except for Podkamennaya Tunguska and Ussuri, the craters listed in the table were formed, as we have mentioned, a great many thousands of years in the past. Just how many thousands is a difficult question to answer, for all of our estimates must necessarily be made on the basis of *indirect* evidence rather than on *direct* observation.

Paleontologists, geologists, and other scientists give us an

Before impact of Canyon Diablo meteorite, these rock layers were horizontal.

age of from 20,000 to 70,000 years for the Canyon Diablo crater. The discovery of the fossil remains of a prehistoric horse
buried in the Odessa, Texas, crater fill has shown that the age
of that crater is not less than 200,000 years. The oldest craters
known in the United States are the Haviland group produced by
the Brenham, Kansas, meteorites. Long-continued weathering
has almost completely worn down the rims and covered up the
craters of this group. On the basis of the rate at which nickel-
oxide has spread out into the soil about a large deeply buried
Brenham meteorite, calculations carried out at the Institute
of Meteoritics have led to a tentative age of more than 600,000
years for the Kansas craters.

Perhaps the oldest meteorite crater of all is the one blasted
into what the geologists identify as pre-Cambrian quartzite at
Wolf Creek, Western Australia. Even the highly resistant iron
meteorites found around this crater have almost completely
weathered away. Only tiny specks and thin veinlets of metal
are now visible on the cut surfaces of meteorites that, untold
hundreds of thousands of years ago, were solid masses of nickel-
iron.

You may have noticed that the widely publicized circular,
water-filled Chubb crater in the Quebec Province of Canada
was not included in the table. This Canadian feature was left
out because the answer to each of the three questions listed
earlier in this chapter is no.

The field parties that have carefully searched the Chubb
crater and its surroundings, even when they used one of the
Institute's powerful drag magnets, were unable to find any trace

COURTESY OF WILLIAM A. CASSIDY

Two of the deeply weathered meteorites found at Wolf Creek crater in western Australia.

whatever either of meteorites or of such weathered remains of meteorites as show the true nature of the Wolf Creek crater. Furthermore, no searcher has discovered any fragments of ordinary rock showing the effects of the extreme heat and pressure that accompany large-scale meteoritic impact. Finally, the meteorite supposed by some to have produced the Chubb crater was not a recorded witnessed fall, for the crater is of very ancient origin indeed.

Perhaps further search of the Chubb crater site and especially of the debris in its deep, water-filled interior will succeed in bringing to light either specimens of meteorites or of silica-glass or other products of meteoritic impact. If so, then and only then will identification of the Canadian crater as a meteorite crater be justified.

Up to this point, we have talked only of very old meteorite craters. But two crater-producing meteorite falls have occurred within this century, both in Siberia. The Ussuri fall was one of these and the more recent of the two.

The earlier and more unusual fall took place on June 30, 1908, at about 8:00 a.m., approximately 40 miles northwest of the trading post of Vanovara. A fireball exceeding the sun in brilliance flashed across the sky and was followed by extremely violent airwaves and earth-tremors.

The pressure wave in the atmosphere set up by this meteorite fall was strong enough to damage roofs and doors of houses near the point of impact, as for example, in the village of Vanovara. On both rivers and lakes in the area of fall, the pressure wave in the air piled up high, sharp-fronted water waves that re-

Oceanside Public Library

sembled the bores on the Seine and Severn and that upset fishing craft and swamped other small boats. Throughout a wide region at somewhat greater distances from the impact point, tidal-like bores were raised on rivers and lakes. So gigantic was the atmospheric disturbance, that it was detected at almost every station in the world where sufficiently sensitive barometers were in operation.

Eyewitnesses of this meteorite fall said that at the time the fireball passed near them, they felt almost unbearable heat.

A huge "fiery pillar" rose above the point of impact, which by good fortune was in a desolate and almost uninhabited swampy basin between the Chunya and the Podkamennaya (i.e., "Stony") Tunguska rivers. The meteorite fall takes its name from the latter stream.

The central portion of the region of impact is marked not only by a number of craters in the swampy terrain, but also by mute evidence of the extraordinary destructive power of the Podkamennaya Tunguska meteorite. Over an area of many square miles, the explosion blew down the standing forest so that the tops of the overthrown trees (estimated by the Russians to number more than 80,000,000!) all point away from the impact center. The intense heat charred the trunks and branches of the trees in this area in much the same way as the heat from the first of all atomic bomb explosions scorched the desert shrubs around the test site in south-central New Mexico.

Within the area of fall, countless reindeer belonging to the native Tunguse herdsmen were killed, only their charred carcasses remaining. How great the heat released at impact was may be judged by the well-established fact that the prized silver samovars of the nomads were found melted amid the debris of their flattened camps. In at least one instance, a Tunguse was so overcome by the terrible event he had witnessed that he was "sick for a long time." The whole impact-region came to be considered as accursed by the natives, who abandoned the use of all trails crossing it.

For many years the Podkamennaya Tunguska fall was neglected, partly because of the remoteness of the area in which it occurred, partly because of unsettled conditions in Russia; but chiefly because, in general, the Russian scientific and governmental officials simply did not believe the "fantastic" tales concerning the fall told by the native Tunguses, from which we have given a few details above.

Belated study established, however, both the truthfulness of the Tunguse reports and the exceedingly unusual character of the meteorite fall itself. In spite of the overwhelming and, in fact, worldwide evidence that the Podkamennaya Tunguska fall was one of the greatest and most violent in history, no meteorites have ever been recovered from any part of the region devastated by its impact. It is the one and only true meteorite crater that is meteoriteless!

This strange circumstance led the senior author to suggest, in 1941, that the almost incredible Podkamennaya Tunguska incident had resulted from the infall of a meteorite that, together with an equivalent mass of the earth-target, was transformed into energy upon contact with our planet. How can such extraordinary behavior be accounted for?

LEONID A. KULIK PHOTO. SOVFOTO

Infall of meteorite, June 30, 1908, had this effect on a Siberian forest. See p. 55.

The most obvious explanation involves a new and wider concept of matter. Ordinary terrestrial matter is regarded as composed of atoms having positively charged nuclei around which negatively charged electrons revolve.

Suppose that the situation shown in the first diagram were reversed so that the nucleus of the atom were negatively charged and the charges of the particles revolving about it were positive, as in the second diagram. Matter built up from atoms like those in this diagram would bear somewhat the same relation to ordinary matter that -2 does to $+2$. Such matter is now known variously as *reversed* matter, *anti*-matter, or, as it was first called by V. Rojansky, *contraterrene* matter. In recent years, scientists at the University of California Radiation Laboratory have produced experimentally all the fundamental particles necessary for the creation of contraterrene matter.

What would happen now if a contraterrene meteorite penetrated into the ordinary matter of the earth? The answer is that just as an electron and a positron mutually annihilate each other when they collide, so the meteorite and an equal mass of the earth-target itself would vanish at the instant of impact. The nearest simple analogy to the actual complex physical situation is represented by the familiar equation $-2 + 2 = 0$.

Unlike "summing to zero" in simple arithmetic, however, the disappearance of mass, technically called its annihilation, results in a release of energy, as was long ago observed in the case of electron-positron annihilation. Where considerable masses are annihilated, as in an A-bomb explosion, the amount of energy released is tremendous, as is now well known to everyone.

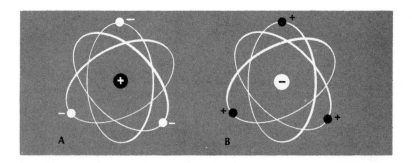

A. Representation of the structure of an atom of ordinary terrestrial matter. The nucleus is positively charged and around it circle negatively charged electrons.

B. Representation of the structure of an atom of contraterrene matter. This is the reverse of the situation in (**A**). The nucleus here is negatively charged, and around it revolve positively charged electrons, also called positrons.

The effect of such an energy release as would accompany the infall of a contraterrene meteorite would be a *natural* nuclear explosion of vast power. Such an explosion would account for all the sensational phenomena observed at the time of the Podkamennaya Tunguska incident; and, furthermore, would explain why the Russian investigators have never succeeded in recovering meteorites from this fall. (Further details, p. 102.)

If the Podkamennaya Tunguska meteorite was contraterrene, then the soil in the impact area must have been made radioactive in the same way that the earth around the "ground zero" of a nuclear explosion is contaminated by radioactivity. After the senior author had repeatedly urged Russian scientists (who are the only ones that have been permitted to visit the site of the Podkamennaya Tunguska fall) to try to detect any long-lasting radioactivities that might still be present in the ground at Podkamennaya Tunguska, such a radioactivity survey was finally carried out in the summer of 1960. According to an official report of the Soviet news agency TASS, the investigators obtained "abnormally high radioactivity readings" which the Russians tentatively considered to be the result of "a natural nuclear explosion" occurring in the Podkamennaya Tunguska area on June 30, 1908.

Science-fiction fans in the U.S.S.R. would like to believe that this "nuclear explosion" resulted from the impact of a Martian spaceship rather than a contraterrene meteorite. Reputable Russian scientists, however, have shown how completely absurd this "fable" of a Martian landing really is.

When and where will the next crater-producing fall occur? Perhaps on the earth, perhaps on the moon, for our nearest neighbor in space has also been the target of meteorites of huge size. The effects of this meteoritic bombardment are shown by the rarest and most striking type of lunar crater: that which exhibits long, bright rays extending outward from the crater itself as the spokes of a wheel radiate from its hub. These so-called *ray-craters* show to best advantage at or near the time of full

G. W. RICHEY PHOTO, COURTESY OF YERKES OBSERVATORY

The lunar ray-crater Tycho.

moon, when they become one of the most remarkable features visible on our satellite.

In earlier days, most scientists believed that the craters on the moon had *all* been formed by volcanic action. Now the pendulum of scientific opinion seems to have swung toward the view that *all* the thousands of lunar craters are the result of meteorite impacts that took place in the long distant past. Both views are better examples of how scientific "fashions" control men's minds than they are of explanations that really account for all of the observed facts—as any acceptable explanation must do.

Those who have studied the moon most carefully from an uncomfortable seat in a cold observatory rather than from a warm, comfortable armchair are well aware that instead of just one type of lunar crater, there are really *two* quite distinct types. No single "explanation" can be expected to explain satisfactorily lunar features as strikingly different as:

First, the rare and distinctive *ray-craters* described above, which are scattered at random over the moon, just as the points of impact of meteorites are upon our own globe. (Roughly defined, a random distribution is one showing no apparent pattern. For example, if you were to throw a handful of rice up in the air, the points where the grains of rice finally came to rest on the floor would be randomly distributed or very nearly so.)

Second, the ordinary or "run-of-the-mill" craters sprinkled in profuse but non-random fashion over the visible face of our satellite.

The ray-craters on the moon are the counterparts of the meteorite craters on the earth. This fact is shown not only by their random distribution, but by the long, bright rays which gave them their name. On the earth, rays of similar appearance, composed of thrown-out material, are one of the most characteristic features of explosion craters, whether the cause of the explosion is the high-speed impact of a great meteorite or the detonation of a charge of high explosive (either conventional or nuclear).

The hypothesis that meteorite craters do exist on the moon is therefore justified even though it applies to far fewer craters than its supporters believe.

As for the ordinary, non-ray lunar craters, these features are not at all volcanic craters in the usual sense. One of the few good things to come out of World War II was the first satisfactory explanation of the "run-of-the-mill" craters on the moon. Jeremi Wasiutynski, a brilliant Polish scientist forced to take refuge in Norway, sought to explain these craters as originating in *convection* processes.

While the term "convection" may not be familiar, the role convection plays in filling the sky with beautiful clouds on a hot summer's day is well known. Such cloud formation results from convection in the gaseous free atmosphere. Much more remarkable and regular are the results of *controlled* convection in layers of *liquids* rather than gases. Laboratory investigation of the effects produced by convection processes in heated liquids formed the basis for Wasiutynski's new theory.

According to this theory, convection processes in the only partially solidified outer shell of the youthful moon could have given rise to great numbers of surface features having the size, shape, and distribution of the common lunar craters. In far more satisfactory fashion than any other theory so far proposed, the convection-current hypothesis of Wasiutynski explains the many and distinctive characteristics of the non-ray craters on the moon.

RECOGNIZED METEORITE CRATERS OF THE WORLD

NAME	LOCATION	DATE OF RECOGNITION
Canyon Diablo	Coconino County, Arizona	1905
Odessa	Ector County, Texas	1929
Henbury	McDonnell Ranges, Central Australia	1932
Wabar	Rub' al Khali, Arabia	1932
Campo del Cielo	Gran Chaco, Argentina	1933
*Haviland (Brenham)	Kiowa County, Kansas	1933
Mount Darwin	Tasmania	1933
**Podkamennaya Tunguska	Yeniseisk District, Siberia	1933
Box Hole Station	Plenty River, Central Australia	1937
Kaalijarv	Oesel, Estonia	1937
Dalgaranga	Western Australia	1938
Ussuri (Sikhote-Alin)	Eastern Siberia	1947
Wolf Creek	Wyndham, Kimberley, Western Australia	1948
Aouelloul	Adrar, Western Sahara	1952

* The meteorites from this crater-producing fall have been found in both Haviland and Brenham Townships, Kiowa County, Kansas. Either of these names may therefore appear in the literature.
** The meteoritic impact nature of the smaller craters found in the central area of the Podkamennaya Tunguska fall has been and continues to be doubted by some authorities.

5. HEAVEN KNOWS WHERE OR WHEN

METEORITES have been falling upon our planet for a long time—how long, it is hard to say with accuracy. Up to now, no specimens certainly identified as meteorites have been found in ancient rock layers. Scientists have been able, however, to estimate the age of several meteorite craters on the basis of the degree of weathering not only of the crater rims, but also of the meteorites found around the craters. Age estimates have also been based on the ages of fossils found in silted-up crater interiors and on other related indirect evidence.

As we have already noted, the Canyon Diablo, Arizona, crater is thought to be 20,000 to 70,000 years old. The Odessa, Texas, crater is at least 200,000 years old; and the Haviland (Brenham), Kansas, craters more than 600,000 years old. Clearly, meteorite falls have been occurring over a very long period of earth history.

For many years, scientists have studied the distribution of recovered meteorites around the world in an effort to find out whether there are any places on the land surface of our globe where meteorites have fallen in unusually large numbers.

The idea that any particular spot on the land surface of the earth might in some way attract more meteorites to it than other locations seems unreasonable because of the very nature of the target presented by our planet to the meteorites wandering through space. Not only is the earth in motion, but it is in very complicated motion. Our earth revolves about a sun which is also in motion through space. At the same time, the earth is rotating on its axis. A single point on the surface of the earth therefore traces a very erratic path in space with the passage of the years, and the likelihood that this particular point would be struck by more than one meteorite (if indeed by one!) must be very small.

Studies have shown that the people of the earth have a great deal more to do with "concentrations" of meteorite recoveries than anything else. *Population density* is the first important factor. Clearly, the more people living in a given area, the higher the probability that a meteorite fall will be seen and reported and that the fallen mass itself will be recovered. A prime example is India, one of the most densely populated regions of the world. Of the 102 meteorites recovered in that country up to 1953, 97 were of witnessed fall. This extremely high proportion of falls is undoubtedly due to the fact that for centuries such an event could hardly have taken place in that country without attracting the attention of large numbers of people. Apparently, the majority of Indian meteorites have been recovered as they fell, for only 5 unwitnessed falls are recorded for that country.

On the other hand, from French West Africa only 5 falls and 3 finds have been reported throughout an area slightly larger even than India's. This country thus provides an example of a sparsely populated region, in many provinces of which a meteorite fall might pass unobserved, and a fallen meteorite might remain undiscovered.

A second factor is the *degree of civilization* reached by the inhabitants of a particular area. Those regions of the world which have been settled the longest and which have seen the development of the higher cultures will be the most likely to support a populace that will take an interest in and report the occurrences of natural events like meteorite falls. Such a populace will also be more likely to bring suspected meteorites to the attention of experts.

For example, up to 1953, 55 witnessed falls and 3 unwitnessed falls were known from France, a country of relatively small area, but with a high population density and an advanced degree of civilization. From the whole vast area of Siberia, on the other hand, only 20 meteorite falls and 23 finds have been reported during the same interval.

In the past, scientists have suggested that various natural forces, such as the magnetic field of the earth or the attraction of high and massive mountain ranges, might cause more meteorites to fall in one place than another. But all available evidence indicates that this is not the case. The fall of meteorites upon the earth has been and is a process that shows no apparent pattern. Only "human" factors (like population density and scientific interest in meteorites) can be considered as accounting for any concentrations of meteorite falls in particular regions or countries.

In historic times, the number of man-built structures (houses, barns, hotels, office buildings, etc.) has increased tremendously. Such structures have presented an ever-expanding target to hits by falling meteorites. On pages 73, 74 is a listing of some of the meteorites that have struck and damaged buildings during the last 150 years or so. The items included in this list were chosen on the basis of interest, authenticity, and concreteness of detail.

The stories of all these meteorite falls are exciting, but none more so, perhaps, than that of the Beddgelert, North Wales, stone. This meteorite fell in the small hours of the morning on September 21, 1949. Not many people saw the fireball that accompanied its descent because of the early hour (1:45 a.m.), but one of the few persons who happened to be outside said that it resembled a huge rocket as it flashed across the sky. He also reported that the appearance of the fireball nearly frightened the swans in the local park to death, the birds fleeing in all directions.

The manager of one of the hotels in Beddgelert simultaneously was awakened from a sound sleep by the barking of his dog. This was an unusual occurrence, and the man was surprised by it. While he was trying to account for the dog's peculiar behavior, he suddenly realized that something quite out of the ordinary was happening outside. He heard a series of unevenly spaced bangs that he later compared to "a naval broadside." But as the noise died away and nothing further happened, he went back to sleep.

About noon on the next day, the manager's wife went into the upstairs lounge of the hotel, a room right under a part of the roof. She was astonished to find plaster dust all over the floor. It had obviously come from a jagged hole in the ceiling. And, on the floor, she found an odd-looking dark stone.

Investigation showed that this stone had indeed fallen through the roof. It had made a neat round hole in four overlapping thicknesses of slate, shattered the underlying lath, made a dent in the lower edge of an H-section iron girder, and had finally broken through the plaster ceiling into the hotel's upstairs lounge.

Although it was clear that the stone had come through the roof, the hotel manager did not connect the event in any way with the peculiar noises he had heard during the preceding night.

He tried to cut the stone on an emery wheel, but it was too hard.

That evening, an old miner in the hotel restaurant recognized the stone as a meteorite. Many years before, he had visited a museum and had seen specimens of meteorites on display there.

The slabs of slate penetrated by the meteorite would have provided good evidence as to the speed of the cosmic missile at the time it struck the roof. But, unfortunately, these appear to have been thrown away at the time the roof was repaired. This fact is mentioned to show that important scientific evidence is sometimes unwittingly destroyed before investigators can get a chance to examine it.

Along with the rapid increase in the number of man-made buildings has, of course, gone a simultaneous increase in the world's population itself. A person does not present as large a target to a falling meteorite as a house or barn, but even so, if there were enough people on the earth, it would seem that someone was bound to be hit sooner or later.

Actually, the first *authentic* case of a person being struck by

G. W. SWINDEL, JR. PHOTO
COURTESY OF ALABAMA MUSEUM OF NATURAL HISTORY

The Sylacauga, Alabama, stone meteorite and the roof (note circle) through which it plunged and struck a person.

a meteorite did not occur until November 30, 1954. Even then, the hit was an indirect one. At Sylacauga, Alabama, a meteorite fell through the roof of a house, went through the ceiling of the living room, struck the top of a radio, and—bouncing in a 6-foot arc—hit the lady of the house, who was taking a nap on the couch. Fortunately, nearly all of the energy of the meteorite was spent by the time it struck the woman, and, moreover, she was covered with two heavy quilts so that she was not critically injured. But she did receive bruises serious enough to send her to the hospital.

The instances just given show that a number of meteorites have struck buildings and, in one case, a cosmic missile has hit a human being. Nevertheless, such events are really quite rare. In fact, mathematical calculations indicate that, on the average, we can expect one meteorite to fall per township (36 square miles) per 1000 years. A rate like this does not justify the loss of any sleep over the possibility that you might some time be hit by a falling meteorite!

SELECTED LIST OF METEORITES THAT HAVE
STRUCK AND DAMAGED BUILDINGS

NAME AND LOCATION	TYPE	APPROXIMATE WEIGHT	YEAR

Baxter, Missouri   stone   611 gm.*   1916
Meteorite penetrated roof and struck a log joist, which checked the fall. The stone lodged in the attic.

Beddgelert, North Wales   stone   794 gm.   1949
Meteorite made a clean hole through 4 thicknesses of slate roof. It then shattered underlying wood, made tiny dent in bottom edge of H-section iron girder, and broke through plaster ceiling into hotel lounge below.

Benld, Illinois   stone   1770 gm.   1938
Meteorite penetrated garage roof, top of car, and seat cushion. It struck and put 1-inch dent in muffler, then bounded back up and became entangled in seat cushion springs.

Bethlehem, New York   stone   11 gm.   1859
Meteorite struck the side of wagon house, bounded off, hit log upon ground, bounded again, and rolled into the grass. (A dog lying in the doorway of the wagon house jumped up, ran out and seized the meteorite, but dropped it right away, probably because of the warmth and sulfurous odor of the stone.)

Branau, Bohemia   iron   19,000 gm.   1847
Meteorite penetrated into room where 3 children were sleeping and covered them with plaster and debris. They were unharmed.

* 453.59 grams = 1 pound.

NAME AND LOCATION	TYPE	APPROXIMATE WEIGHT	YEAR
Constantia, South Africa	stone	999 gm.	1906

Meteorite penetrated 2 thicknesses of corrugated iron roofing and smashed ceiling.

Kasamatsu, Japan	stone	721 gm.	1938

Meteorite penetrated roof of house and stopped on floor. It went through roof tile, ⅓-inch wooden roof-panel, and layer of clay 1 inch thick between them.

Kilbourn, Wisconsin	stone	772 gm.	1911

Meteorite went through 3 thicknesses of shingles, a 1-inch hemlock roof board, and a ⅞-inch hemlock floor board. It then glanced in turn against the side of a manger and the stone foundation of the barn and finally penetrated 2½ inches into the clay floor of the barn.

Pantar, Philippine Is.	stone	shower	1938

Sixteen stones were recovered; thousands "as big as corn and rice grains" fell on roofs.

Sylacauga, Alabama	stone	3863 gm.	1954

Meteorite penetrated composition roof material, ¾-inch wooden decking, ¾-inch wooden ceiling, and interior wallboard. It then hit a radio, punching a 1-inch hole in plywood top, and bounced 90° towards the east, striking woman lying on couch.

6. FINDERS FOOLISH, FIND-ERS WISE

PEOPLE FIND a great many meteorites that were not seen to fall. Most of these landed on the surface of the earth at some time in the remote past or happened to fall in an originally un-populated portion of the land area of the globe. Generally, such meteorites are discovered entirely by accident, although in re-cent years quite a few recoveries of unwitnessed falls have been made by design. This has been the case during the systematic surveys with meteorite detectors conducted around such recog-nized meteorite crater areas as Canyon Diablo, Arizona; Odessa, Texas; and Wolf Creek, Australia.

The different modes of discovery of meteorites not seen to fall are interesting in themselves. The largest percentage of finds has unquestionably been made by farmers. The Plymouth, In-diana, meteorite, for example, was plowed up or, as the farmer nursing the rib bruised by his bucking plow would probably prefer to say, "plowed into." So were such meteorites as the Algoma, Wisconsin; the Bridgewater, North Carolina; the Carl-ton, Texas; and the Chesterfield, South Carolina, to name only a few. A farmer found the Kenton, Kentucky, iron while he was cleaning out a spring. Another farmer was removing debris from an abandoned water well in an attempt to revive it when he discovered the Richland, Texas, iron. A field drainage project brought the Seeläsgen, Poland, iron to light. A man planting an apple tree near his house dug out the Mount Joy, Pennsylvania, iron, and a farmer hoeing tobacco turned up the Scottsville, Kentucky, iron.

The second largest percentage of finds probably has been made by miners. Prospectors and placer miners have mistaken numerous iron meteorites for lumps of silver ore. Among these are the Murfreesboro, Tennessee; Lick Creek, North Carolina; and Illinois Gulch, Montana, irons. The Aggie Creek, Alaska, iron was raised by a gold dredge. The gold miners recognized this meteorite as an unusual "haul" when it announced its presence by clanging loudly on the metallic screen of the dredge.

Men at work on road construction are also to be thanked for chancing upon meteorites of unwitnessed fall, for example, the irons found by road crews at Bear Lodge, Wyoming, and at Bald Eagle, Pennsylvania.

Some meteorites have been "found twice." At Opava, Czechoslovakia, archeologists discovered seven pieces of meteoritic iron in a buried Stone Age campsite—the oldest meteorite collection so far on record! Apparently the paleolithic inhabitants of the Opava region had gathered the heavy masses together and used them to bolster the fireplaces in their rude encampment.

Investigators discovered the Mesaverde, Colorado, iron in the Sun Shrine on the north side of the Pipe Shrine House, and the Casas Grandes, Mexico, iron in the middle of a large room of the Montezuma temple ruins, carefully wrapped in linen cloth like a mummy. Members of an early archeological survey found the small Anderson Township, Ohio, meteoritic specimens on altars in mounds of the Little Miami Valley group of prehistoric earthworks. Some scientists believe that the American Indians

The Lake Murray, Oklahoma, iron meteorite in place, just as it was found. See p. 80.

transported these specimens to Ohio from the site of the Brenham meteorites in Kiowa County, Kansas.

Other modes of discovery fall into no pattern and must be
regarded as merely curious. A farmer plowing his field near
Pittsburgh, Pennsylvania, came across a snake. In looking for a
suitable stone with which to kill it, he first seized upon a mass
of iron too heavy to lift. After he had killed the snake with a
handy rock, the farmer's attention was drawn back to the small
but remarkably heavy mass he had first tried to pick up. He
carted it off to the city, where eventually it was recognized as
a meteorite.

In another unusual recovery, fishermen brought the Lake
Okeechobee, Florida, stone up from the waters of the lake in
a net—the only such recovery recorded in the whole literature
of meteoritics, although three-fourths of all meteorites must necessarily fall into water on our ocean-covered globe. Again, the
members of the Australasian Antarctic Expedition of 1911-1914
were surprised to find the Adelie Land, Antarctica, stone lying
on the snow some 20 miles west of Cape Denison.

Because the true nature of meteorite finds has often been
unrecognized—sometimes for many years—these masses have
been put to some rather lowly uses. The finder of the Rafrüti,
Switzerland, iron meteorite used it as a footwarmer, and many
of the heavy irons have been employed as haystack, fence, and
barrel-cover weights, or as anvils, nutcrackers, and doorstops.

Some have fared better, as did the 1,375-pound La Caille,
France, meteorite, which the people of the village used for two
centuries as a seat in front of their church. Others, however,

It's a whopper! See p. 80.

have fared even worse. Blacksmiths and assayers have smelted up and destroyed a number of iron meteorites either in the making of tools (like plowshares, axe-heads, and knife-blades) or in the quest for precious metals. Nearly all of the iron meteorite that was found by the farmer near Pittsburgh was worked up by a blacksmith and lost to science. Even the stone meteorites have occasionally fallen victims to man's greed for gold. Miners who believed that the 80-pound San Emigdio, California, stony meteorite was gold-bearing mashed it to powder in an ore-crusher.

On the contrary, people who, in one way or another, have become acquainted with the characteristics of meteorites have brought a number of these objects to the attention of scientists. For example, one of the University of Nebraska men who worked on the excavation and removal of the large Furnas County stone meteorite (see Chapter 2) became keenly interested at that time in meteorites in general, and took the trouble to learn as much as he could about them. Several years later, after he had become director of a state park museum in southern Oklahoma, a large metallic mass was reported to him. The finder of this mass of metal had known of its existence for some 20 years, but had never succeeded in getting anyone to examine it carefully. The former field worker took one look at the object and, on the basis of his knowledge of meteorites, concluded that it probably was a huge iron meteorite. He immediately called the Institute of Meteoritics by long distance and was able to give such a wealth of significant details that a field party left at once for the site. In this way, the Lake Murray, Oklahoma, meteorite was identified and recovered.

The Lake Murray core mounted on the meteorite saw which cut it in half. One of the worn soft iron saw-blades is held above the meteorite by the saw guides. See pp. 167, 168.

The unoxidized central core of this iron weighed more than 600 pounds. Before excavation this core was surrounded by a "shell" of oxidized meteoritic material several inches thick, as shown on page 77. Such a shell of oxide clearly indicated that the meteorite had been subjected to weathering in the ground for many thousands of years.

In general, meteorites *seen to fall*—possibly because of the magnitude and impressiveness of the light and sound effects connected with their descent—have received respectful treatment after recovery. Most of them have been presented to men of science for study and eventual display in some museum collection. Even when kept by their finders, the specimens usually have been well cared for. After the fall of the Flows, North Carolina, meteorite in 1849, the owner of the land on which it came down set the stone in a place of honor on top of a barrel fixed to a post. On the post he put up the notice:

> *"Gentlemen, sirs—please not to break this rock,*
> *which fell from the skies and weighs 19.5 pounds."*

This landowner obviously realized that nearly everyone has the unfortunate urge to hammer on strange rocks.

Of course, there have been exceptions to the respectful treatment of meteorites seen to fall. The finder of one fragment of the Zhovtnevy Hutor, Russia, fall tossed it into the stove, and a farm woman lost another by throwing it at an unruly horse. A peasant who thought meteorites possessed miraculous powers powdered up a piece of the diamond-bearing Novo-Urei, Russia, stone and ate it!

A polished and etched face of the Lake Murray meteorite. The length of the cut is a good 23 inches.

7. LANDMARKS, SKYMARKS & DETECTORS

THE CHEMIST can easily obtain materials for his research work from reliable supply houses. The meteoriticist (as a scientist who studies meteors and meteorites is known), is not this lucky. He must search for the specimens he wishes to investigate wherever they may have landed on the wide, wide earth. This "needle-in-a-haystack" problem could rarely be solved if it were not for certain mathematical and instrumental aids that swing the balance in favor of the meteorite hunter. When meteorites are seen to fall, these aids can be brought into play only if certain information is supplied by eyewitnesses of the falls. For this reason, everyone ought to be acquainted with the facts about meteorite falls that scientists will need to know in order to make finds, and should understand how these facts must be reported in order to be of maximum use to field parties.*

The problem of working out the path a fireball has followed in the sky boils down to this. The investigating scientists must be able to fix the position *in space* of certain important points on the fireball's path. This idea of fixing points is not really difficult at all. Suppose, to take an analogy from baseball, we have base runners on first and third. These two players are intently watching their team's clean-up hitter, who is "crowding the plate." Consequently their lines of sight intersect at home plate

* A questionnaire for making an adequate report is obtainable by request from the Institute of Meteoritics, The University of New Mexico, Albuquerque.

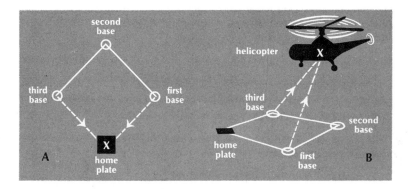

A. A fix determined in two dimensions. The lines of sight of the runners on first and third intersect at **x**.

B. A fix determined in three dimensions. The lines of sight of the runners on the first and third intersect at **x**.

and give a very good "fix on" its position, as navigators say. This is the way a fix can be obtained in *two* dimensions; that is, essentially, in the plane of the earth's surface.

Now, let us move into the *third* dimension, since a fireball's path through the atmosphere lies in space, not in the "flat" plane of the earth's surface. Returning to our baseball diamond, let us suppose that a helicopter with an enterprising photographer aboard hovers over the centerfield bleachers so that he can take pictures of the record crowd. While the umpire is dusting off home plate, the two runners on first and third simultaneously sneak a look to see what the helicopter is doing. Their lines of sight now intersect at the helicopter and fix its position *in space.*

Similarly, the location of a fireball path in space is determined by the fixing of certain points on the luminous streak seen in the sky. Instead of using only two intersecting lines of sight (those of the runners on first and third in our analogy), scientists investigating a meteorite fall try to collect as many different lines of sight as possible from people in the region above which the fireball streaked. The more commonly determined points are those of the fireball's appearance and disappearance and those where "explosions" took place. These points are generally located by use of the method we have described in some detail above, the so-called *intersecting-lines-of-sight* method.

The most important point on a fireball path is the point of disappearance. The most valuable single piece of information you can supply about a meteorite fall is as accurate an answer as possible to the question: In what compass direction were you looking when you *last* saw the fireball? This question has often been twisted around in newspaper and radio accounts into the meaningless question: In what direction was the fireball going when you saw it?

One person cannot give the answer to the second question because from a single station it is impossible to determine the *true* direction of motion of an object seen in the sky. One person can report only an *apparent* direction of motion, which is of little or no value in locating the last point on the luminous path, generally referred to as the "end-point." Therefore, though you cannot by yourself determine the actual direction in which a fireball is *moving,* you can report the direction in which you

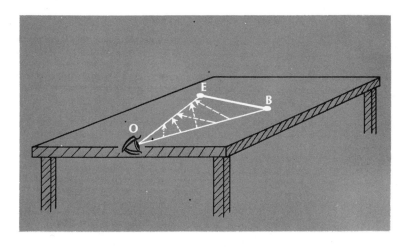

O is an observer squinting along the top of a ping-pong table. A ping-pong ball rolls along the top of the table from **B** (beginning) to **E** (end). To the observer at **O**, however, the ball would appear to start at **B** and end at **E** if it rolled along any one of the dashed lines leading from **OB** to **OE**. By means of a similar space-figure, it can be shown that a single observer at **O** cannot determine the *true* direction of motion of a luminous object in the sky, like a meteor.

were *looking* when you last saw the fireball, that is, due south, southwest, northeast, etc.

Scientists are eager to obtain reliable reports on the compass direction to the fireball's point of disappearance from as many widely separated eyewitnesses as possible. They then can plot the individual lines of sight on a good map, marking exactly where these lines intersect. In this way, the investigators can make reasonably accurate fixes of the position of the point on the earth's surface that is situated directly below the end-point of the fireball path, as this end-point was seen in the sky by each pair of eyewitnesses.

Instead of using the ordinary compass direction to a fireball's point of disappearance, you may prefer, as do astronomers, to use the azimuth. What we have been calling a "compass direction" is one that is expressed in terms of the cardinal points: north, south, east, west. An azimuth is a direction stated in *degrees*. Rough azimuths can be taken with a compass, but for accurate work, a graduated circle, like that on a transit or theodolite, must be used. Astronomical azimuths begin at the *south* point and continue clockwise full circle to 360°. For example, the lines of sight in the diagram, p. 87, could very well have been given as astronomical azimuths. And, in the diagram, p. 91, the line of sight C_1 could have had the precise designation 118° and C_2 that of 222°.

Every fix serves to guide field parties to areas that are to be carefully searched for fallen meteorites. Extra-thorough searches are made if the people living in a particular area reported that they heard meteorite fragments hissing and whining on their way to earth or heard the thumps of their impacts on the ground.

You will notice that so far we have been treating our problem as a two-dimensional one. We have been working with *directions* only and have plotted out direction indicators on a map representing the plane of the earth's surface. Now, as we did in our baseball analogy, let us move into the third dimension.

If, in addition to compass directions to the observed end-

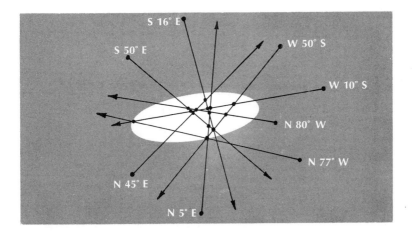

Diagram (not drawn to scale) showing plotted compass directions to the last visible point on a fireball path. (The point denoted by **L** in next diagram.) Black dots represent positions of various observers. Each arrowed line is directed toward the last visible point as it was estimated by the individual observer. The oval area, which includes points of intersection of all observed lines of sight taken in pairs, marks out region in which meteorites have probably fallen.

point, scientists can also obtain the apparent *elevation,* in degrees, of this point as seen by the various eyewitnesses, then with the help of a little trigonometry, they can fix the position *in space* of the end-point itself rather than the position of its *projection* on the surface of the earth.

This same procedure can be followed in fixing the space-position of any well-observed point on the fireball path. It therefore becomes possible when *both* elevations and compass directions are reported for several points on the fireball path to determine the flight-path or, as it is technically called, the *trajectory,* of the falling meteorite through the atmosphere. Trajectory determinations are of great scientific value.

You can estimate the compass directions and elevations to the important points on a meteorite trajectory at the actual time of fall. Or you can have the scientific field party make or check your measurement at some later time by setting up a surveying instrument at the very point from which you saw the fireball.

The accuracy of your measurements can be improved if you have been able to "line up" the point, L, at which you saw the fireball disappear, with some familiar object on the horizon, such as a church steeple, a tall tree, a telephone pole, or a lightning rod on a farm building. You will recall that an eleven-year old girl provided one of the field parties from the Institute of Meteoritics with an excellent observation of the point of disappearance of the Norton fireball. She was able to do this because she remembered just where it went out of sight behind a familiar landmark.

If the fall occurs at night, you can help investigators greatly

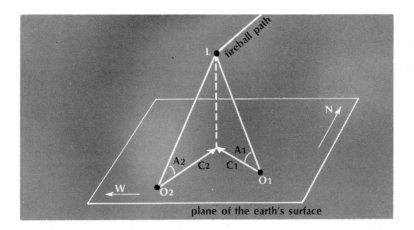

Method for locating a point on a fireball path. (In this case the point of disappearance, **L**.)

O₁ First observer.

A₁ Apparent height of point of disappearance (50°).

C₁ Compass direction of point of disappearance (N 62° W).

O₂ Second observer.

A₂ Apparent height of point of disappearance (45°).

C₂ Compass direction of point of disappearance (N 42° E).

if you are familiar enough with the brighter stars to use them as "skymarks." You simply note as quickly and sharply as you can just where the fireball path was in reference to those prominent stars. This alert observation of yours will at least be a great aid to investigators who are searching for meteorites that may have fallen from the fireball; and, moreover, there is no telling what else your quick eye might have captured for science.

While looking through a window, Kayser, the Polish astronomer, saw a fireball appear at Rigel and move to Sirius, where it disappeared. This observation of his proved to be one of the most accurate and *significant* ever made of the fall of a meteorite. For it enabled the German mathematician, Galle, to show that the Pultusk meteorite, which produced the fireball Kayser saw, came into the Solar System from interstellar space!

It is very essential to carefully notice and mark the exact spot from which your observation was made so that you can return to it if scientists wish to set up surveying instruments there.

The map and side view of the Norton County, Kansas, meteorite trajectory show the practical results that the Institute obtained by use of the intersecting-lines-of-sight method. The fireball accompanying the Norton meteorite fall appeared at A. The first "explosion" took place at E_1, the second at E_2, and the fireball disappeared at L.

If markers were dropped straight down to earth from each point along the trajectory or flight-path of a meteorite through the atmosphere, the line joining the points where the markers fell would be the *earth-trace* of this trajectory. The directions of sight to these various points are indicated for people living in

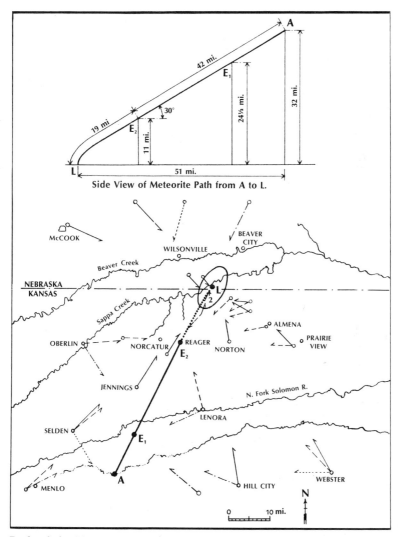

Side View of Meteorite Path from A to L.

Path of the Norton meteorite.

the towns along and near the earth-trace of the Norton meteorite fall. The solid-line arrows represent the direction of the point of disappearance; the dotted-line arrows, the point of appearance; the dash-dot arrows, E_1; and the dashed arrows, E_2. The probable area of fall is shown as an oval-shaped area, the longer axis of which is identical with the direction of motion of the meteorite.

The many fragments of all sizes recovered from the Norton fall were all found within the bounds of this oval-shaped area, although unavoidable errors of observation placed the center of the oval about 4 miles too far to the north.

In addition to the questions about direction and elevation, there are a few more that investigators of meteorite falls would like to have observers answer.

At what time (determined as accurately as possible) did the fall occur? Knowledge of this time is necessary if the path in which the meteorite was moving about the sun is to be calculated by scientists.

Did you hear any sounds, either while you were watching the fireball or after it disappeared? If you heard such sounds as the whining or hissing of meteorite fragments flying through the air or the heavy thumps of their impacts on the earth, then you were very close to where the meteorite came down!

How many minutes and seconds (again determined as accurately as you can) passed between the time when you saw the fireball vanish and the instant when you first heard sounds from it? Such sound data permit rough determination of the distance from the observer to the point where the meteorite fell.

How long did the sounds set up by the meteorite last, and in what direction did these sounds seem to die out?

If you or your neighbors find fragments that you suspect are pieces of the meteorite, these specimens should be shown to the investigating field parties at once—preferably undisturbed and in the very places where they fell. In any event, the suspect masses should not be hammered on and broken up! Even as late as 1958 in a country as science-conscious as Germany, a beautiful stony meteorite, seen to fall and speedily found by an alert group of children playing out of doors, was deliberately broken up into 5 pieces in order that each of the children (aged 9 years and up) might take home a "souvenir" of the event. Later, these pieces had to be laboriously reassembled by scientists before any idea could be gained of the original shape and surface features of the meteorite.

Even when thorough searches are made, not all the meteorite fragments in the area of fall may be found for many months. But if the people living in the region have been alerted and are on the lookout for unusual specimens or signs of meteoritic impact (such as freshly made holes or "craters" in the ground, shattered tree limbs, and so forth), the chances of ultimately finding many or most of the fallen masses are good.

As we have already mentioned, numerous fragments of the

Norton meteorite (including one weighing 130 pounds) were found within two to three months after its fall on February 18, 1948. But the main mass was not discovered until the following August, when a caterpillar tractor nearly tipped over into the large impact funnel that this huge stone had made in the earth. Fortunately, field searchers from the Institute had already talked to one of the farmers using the tractor and had told him that just such a "crater" might be found in the very area under cultivation. Consequently, the crater was promptly reported.

In surveys concerned with the location and recovery of meteorites *not* seen to fall, we find that sometimes meteorite fragments, particularly the smaller ones, lie on the surface of the ground or at shallow depth. Such fragments were probably too light to penetrate deep into the ground or, in the years since their fall, the action of rain, wind, and frost has uncovered them.

In such cases, a party of searchers generally spreads out in order to get over as much ground as possible and each member of the group looks for meteorite specimens without using instrumental aids. Visual searches of this type have been very successful, for example, around the Canyon Diablo crater, where almost the entire plain out to several miles from the rim once was sprinkled with large and small fragments of meteoritic nickel-iron. This type of meteorite hunt is of only limited effectiveness because the specimens (or at least a part of each one) must be visible to the searchers.

To increase recoveries, searchers have employed, in addition to their eyes, various types of permanent magnets, either mounted on the end of a cane and used to probe the upper few inches of

Collecting small surface specimens of meteorites with portable detecting devices: a powerful alnico magnet mounted on a light wooden sled, and a horseshoe magnet at the end of a cane. See p. 98.

loose soil, or dragged behind the searcher on a small, light sled. Meteorite hunters have also used more powerful portable electromagnets to collect large amounts of meteoritic material (both solid iron and iron-shale) not only from the surface but also from shallow depths. Even the best of these simple magnetic devices, however, are useless in the detection of really deeply buried meteoritic material.

Meteorites do not merely fall upon the earth (as most astronomical textbooks still insist), but usually penetrate into it—often quite deeply. In fact, one of our mathematical investigations showed that perhaps 100,000 times as much meteoritic nickel-iron is concentrated below maximum plow-depth (approximately one foot) as lies above that depth. Clearly, some form of instrument capable of detecting deeply buried meteorites needed to be devised if this wealth of buried material was not to be lost to science. This need was answered by the development of special *meteorite detectors.*

Although meteorite detectors working on several different principles have been constructed, we shall limit attention here to the simplest and most field-worthy design. The essential principle on which it operates is one familiar to any Boy or Girl Scout who has used a magnetic compass. The first lesson Scoutmasters teach is not to read compass directions from such an instrument when it is held near a mass of iron of considerable size, such as an automobile. Such a large iron mass alters or distorts the local magnetic field of the earth on which the direction-finding ability of the ordinary compass depends. It is this very characteristic, so bothersome to the user of a compass, that

A 146-pound iron, found by this girl without the use of instruments although only a small corner of the meteorite was visible above the surface of the ground.

A commercially built meteorite detector in operation.

Oceanside Public Library

is the principle on which meteorite detectors work. For if an electrically driven meteorite detector capable of generating its own magnetic field is carried over a deeply buried iron meteorite, the instrument's magnetic field will be distorted by the presence of the metal mass, just as the local magnetic field of the earth was distorted by the metal of the automobile.

The operator of such a meteorite detector wears earphones and watches a signal needle in plain sight on the top panel of the detector. Since the phone and signal-needle circuits of the meteorite detector are *in balance* only when the magnetic field generated by the detector is undistorted, the disturbing presence of a deeply buried meteorite is at once revealed by a shrill note sounding in the earphones and simultaneous motion of the signal needle. If, as in all buried treasure stories, we use "X" to stand for the spot where the signals from the detector are strongest, then the meteorite-hunter has only to dig deep enough at "X" to recover the celestial treasure-trove he is after.

8. THE NATURE OF METEORS

IN ANSWER to an exam question, a freshman astronomy student wrote:

> A *meteor* is the flash of light
> Made by a falling *meteorite*
> As it rushes through the air in flight–
> I hope to gosh this answer's right!

Doggerel or not, the student's definition correctly stated the true distinction between the two terms, and the teacher marked his off-beat answer correct.

Defined in more scientific terms, a meteor is the streak of light (usually of brief duration) that accompanies the flight of a particle of matter from outer space through our atmosphere. This particle may be as small as a tiny dust grain or as large as one of the minor planets which are called asteroids. Fortunately for the inhabitants of the earth, most of the meteor-forming masses encountered by our globe are of the "small-fry" variety!

As the rapidly moving particle plunges earthward through denser and denser layers of atmosphere, the air molecules offer ever-increasing resistance to its passage. This resistance heats up the meteorite body until it glows. Technically speaking, it becomes incandescent. *The meteor is this incandescence.* We see it as a darting point. Or as a ball of white, orange, bluish, or reddish light. But the *material object* that produced this light is the *meteorite*. The distinction between these two terms—meteor and meteorite—we must emphasize again and again because people continue to use them incorrectly, as, for instance, when they keep saying "meteor crater" instead of "meteorite crater."

The majority of the meteors we observe represent the heat-induced "evaporation" of exceedingly small fragments of cosmic matter. The smallest meteor-forming bodies reach the surface of the earth only as the finest of dust particles or as microscopic droplets of solidified meteorite melt.

These residues descend slowly through the atmosphere and may be carried for great distances. Afterwards, they may be found scattered so widely and uniformly on the ground that their presence in any given locality cannot be accounted for by the fall of any specific meteorite. This is a fact that, for example, one school of modern Russian meteoriticists overlooked when they were dealing with tiny granules of meteoritic dust that had been recently found at Podkamennaya Tunguska. These scientists tried to identify the tiny granules with the meteorite that had fallen there, June 30, 1908. But the members of the latest (1958) Russian expedition to that region about the impact point of 1908 clearly recognize the widespread character of meteoritic dust. So they reject the theory that such dust found in the Pod-kamennaya Tunguska area is specifically connected with the meteorite that fell there a half century ago.

If sizable chunks of meteoritic material enter the atmosphere, they may produce exceptionally large and brilliant meteors. A spectacular meteor is generally known as a "fireball" if it is as bright as Venus or Jupiter. It receives the French term *bolide* if, in addition to showing great brillance, its flight is accompanied by detonations like the alarming sounds heard at the time of the Ussuri and Norton meteorite falls.

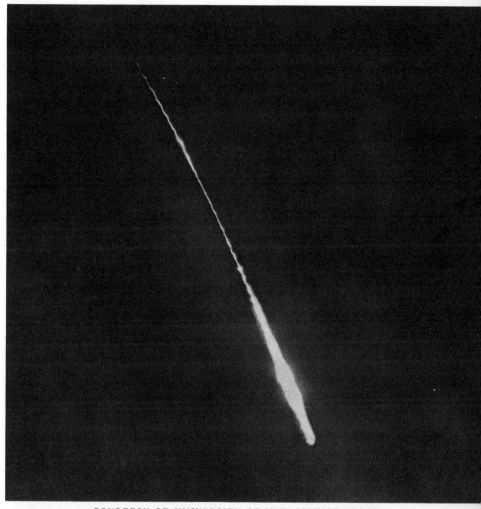

COURTESY OF UNIVERSITY OF NEW MEXICO PRESS

A bright Giacobinid meteor, photographed from a B-29 during the shower of October 9, 1946. See p. 115.

The term "shooting star," which is often applied to meteors, in newspapers and magazine articles, is a misnomer. A meteor is *not* a distant sun (that is, a star) in rapid motion, for the whole path of the meteor lies close at hand within a restricted zone of the earth's atmosphere.

The word "meteor" comes from the Greek word *meteōra,* which once applied to any natural occurrence *in the atmosphere* —for example, rainbows, halos, auroras, and so forth. Nowadays, the word "meteor" is used in a much more specialized sense than it was by the ancient Greeks. We have a specialized word, *meteoritics,* for the study of meteors and meteorites. No one should confuse meteoritics with *meteorology,* which is the science of things *other* than meteors and meteorites, in the atmosphere—for example, clouds, storms, air currents.

The region in which meteoric phenomena take place was long the subject of controversy. Some persons felt that meteors were nearby, like lightning. Others said that they moved at the distances of the remote fixed stars. This controversy on the whereabouts of meteors became heated, although it could have been settled quickly by a simple experiment you can try out for yourself.

Hold a pencil against the tip of your nose and look at it first with your right eye closed and then with your left eye closed. Repeat this experiment with the pencil held at arm's length. In the first case, the pencil will seem to shift position very greatly; in the second, although the same base line (the distance between your eyes) is used, the pencil will seem to shift position only slightly.

Oceanside Public Library

Such an apparent shift in position is called a *parallactic displacement,* or, simply, *parallax.* The notion of parallax is of the greatest importance in most branches of astronomy, and it leads (with proper instruments and a little mathematics) to exact determinations of the distances of remote objects.

For our purpose, we need not go into all the interesting but complicated details. Our experiment with the pencil shows that if a meteor was close by, like a blinding bolt of lightning, then, as seen by a pair of observers separated by only a few blocks, the meteor would show a large parallax. But if this meteor was as far away as the stars, it would show no parallax at all, no matter how widely the pair of observers were separated on the earth.

There were many clever scientists among the Greeks, and it is quite possible that a pair of them actually tried out this simple parallax experiment on the meteors and so were able to prove that these beautiful light effects occurred in the high but not too distant layers of the atmosphere. The earliest calculations of meteor heights that are so far known, however, were made in Bologna, Italy, in 1719 and 1745—long after the heyday of Greek science.

The meteor heights found by the Italians were quite low in the atmosphere, probably for two reasons. First, the visual (unaided-eye) observations they had to use were made by eyewitnesses stationed so close together that accurate fixes were impossible. Secondly, these visual observations must have related only to the very brightest and therefore lowest portions of the luminous paths of the meteors through the atmosphere.

In 1798, two German students operating from carefully chosen and widely separated stations began the systematic observation of meteors for parallax. They found that the height of appearance of most meteors lay between 48 and 60 miles above the earth's surface. It is now known that most meteors, as observed with the naked eye, appear at about 70 miles and disappear at about 50 miles above the surface of the earth. These figures, obtained from visual work, still stand in spite of the development of such modern techniques as photographic and radar recording of meteor paths.

Rarely, meteors may appear at heights of 150 or more miles and fireballs may penetrate to within a few miles of the earth. The average meteors, however, appear and disappear within a well-defined, high-altitude zone in the atmosphere. Fortunately, this atmospheric zone serves us as an effective shield against the constant bombardment of the smaller and much more numerous particles from outer space.

In earlier times, scientists thought that the particles becoming visible as meteors must be tiny dense masses of iron or stone like the material composing the recovered meteorites. Most modern investigators, however, believe that the typical meteor-forming particles may be small loosely bound-together "dust-balls"; that is, fluffy clusters of matter held together by frozen cosmic vapors, generally referred to simply as "ices." In any event, these masses are usually very small, ranging perhaps from the size of a pinhead to that of a marble.

Because we cannot collect the tiny masses that are seen only as meteors, it is impossible to determine their composition by ordinary laboratory methods. The best we can do is to observe and record carefully the light these masses give off when they become incandescent in their plunge through the atmosphere.

We can examine this meteor light by using the spectroscope and spectrograph. Through these specially designed instruments we can make the meteor light reveal the chemical elements present in the incandescent masses. Each such element sends out light rays as characteristic of its nature as fingerprints are of the individual who made them. Photographs taken of these characteristic light rays are called *spectrograms,* and what might be termed the "fingerprints of light" recorded on these spectrograms are known as *spectra*—which is the plural of the word *spectrum*. If the source of light is a meteor, the photograph shows a meteor spectrum.

From a study of a considerable number of good quality meteor spectra, scientists have found that the principal elements in the masses responsible for meteors are iron, calcium, manganese, magnesium, chromium, silicon, nickel, aluminum, and sodium.

As we have already noted, the resistance encountered by meteor-forming particles as they dash through our atmosphere is so great that they become incandescent and vaporize. These small bodies must therefore be in very rapid motion.

Before we attempt to find out the nature of the paths in space followed by meteorites, we must take into account the fact that these bodies are observed from a station—the earth—which is itself in rapid motion. You may have noticed that on a still day, when rain drops fall vertically downward, the streaks they leave

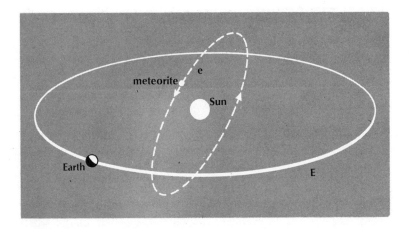

Diagram showing meteorite moving along a "closed" (elliptic) orbit,
e, which intersects the earth's orbit, **E**. Held by the gravitational
attraction of the sun, the meteorite is a permanent member of the
Solar System.

on the windows of a swiftly moving car are not vertical but
almost horizontal. Obviously, it would be wrong to say the rain
drops are falling from left to right or from right to left when they
are actually falling almost straight down, and it is only the forward motion of the car that makes them leave horizontal streaks.

Similarly, neither the apparent speed nor the apparent direction of motion of a meteorite with respect to the moving earth is
significant. The important factor is the meteorite's velocity *with
respect to the sun* at the time the meteorite is picked up by the
earth.

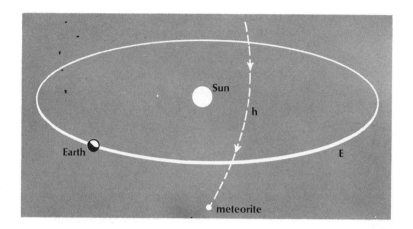

Diagram showing meteorite moving across the earth's orbit, **E**, along an "open" (hyperbolic) orbit, **h**. The meteorite is traveling at such high velocity that it will pass right through the Solar System and back out into space unless it should chance to collide with the earth or another planet. The sun, however, in any case is able to change materially the direction of motion of the transient visitor to our Solar System.

This factor enables us to determine in which of two possible kinds of path the meteorite was moving *before* it was "fielded," as we might say in baseball, by the earth. This factor tells us whether the meteorite was moving about the sun in a relatively short, closed, oval-shaped path or, instead, was following an indefinitely long, open path which began in the depths of space and would have returned there if the collision with the earth had not prevented.

Either type of path is technically called an *orbit*. The closed orbits are what the mathematicians term *ellipses;* the open orbits, *hyperbolas.*

To scientists, the nature of the orbits followed by meteorites is most important, especially in efforts to determine the mode and place of origin of these bodies. To rocket engineers and astronauts, it also matters a good deal whether the meteorites encountered on flights through space are traveling sedately along closed orbits about the sun or are zipping swiftly along open orbits.

The greater the speed of these cosmic "hot-rods," the more dangerous they are to space travelers. For example, a mere grain of nickel-iron moving at 40 miles per second is quite as lethal as a .50-caliber machine-gun slug, which, relatively speaking, is traveling at only a snail's pace.

As our earth moves along its orbit about the sun, meteoritic bodies can run into it from any direction. The direction from which they do approach strongly influences the speed of these bodies as they plunge through the earth's atmosphere. A meteorite moving slowly about the sun in the same direction as the earth and chancing to catch up with our globe more or less from behind will have an observed speed of only a few miles a second. For example, the speed calculated from Harvard meteor-photographs of one such not-too-spectacular "rear-end" collision amounted to no more than 7.3 miles per second, just about the speed a rocket must acquire to escape from the apron strings of Mother Earth.

In contrast to such a "rear-end" collision, the speed observed

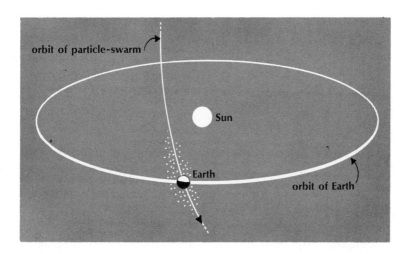

Meteor shower. Earth and particle-swarm passing through the intersection of their orbits at nearly the same moment.

would be far greater if the meteorite happened to collide exactly "head-on" with the earth. For, in this case, the orbital speed of our planet would be *added* to that of the meteorite about the sun. As an example, suppose that at the earth's average distance from the center of our Solar System, the speed of a meteorite with respect to the sun were 32.23 miles per second. (This speed was actually found for the mass that produced one of the first meteors photographed simultaneously by the Harvard stations at Cambridge and Oak Ridge, Massachusetts.) Then if such a meteorite ran "head-on" into the earth, the speed observed for it in the atmosphere would be over 51 miles per second. And mathematics would show that the orbit of this meteorite with respect to the sun was a wide open hyperbola.

If the orbit of the earth and the orbit of a swarm of particles of cosmic matter intersect, and if the earth and the swarm pass through this intersection in space at nearly the same moment, multitudes of meteors appear. We then say that a *meteor shower* takes place. The position of the point at which the particle-swarm crosses the earth's orbit about the sun fixes the date of the meteor shower.

Because the particles that make a meteor shower are moving through space along parallel paths as they come into the earth's atmosphere, the meteors all seem to shoot out from a single small area in the sky. You may have seen something like this in the case of the sunrise or sunset effect known as "the sun drawing water." In this more familiar phenomenon, the sun's disk is the area from which shafts of sunlight radiate out in a beautiful, if somewhat irregular, fan-like pattern. The area from which the meteors of a given shower seem to come is the *radiant* of that shower.

Meteor showers are named for the constellation in which their radiant lies. The suffix "-id" (Greek for "daughters of"), or some modification of this suffix, is added to the name of the constellation from which the meteors seem to radiate. The Orionid radiant, for example, is in Orion, the Hunter; the Leonid radiant is in Leo, the Lion; and the Lyrid radiant is in Lyra, the Harp. Exceptions to this rule do occur, however. Astronomers may refer to a shower sometimes appearing on the night of Oc-

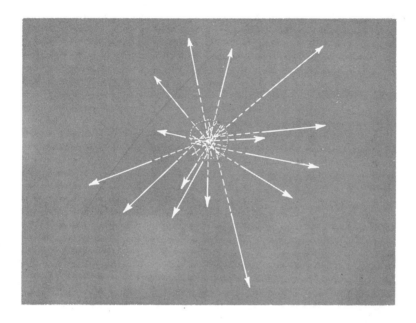

Radiant of a meteor shower. Generally not a point but a small area, here intentionally exaggerated in size. Solid arrows represent plotted paths of observed meteors. By extending these paths backwards, observer can determine the radiant.

tober 9 as the "Giacobinid" shower in honor of the comet Gia-cobini-Zinner, which is associated with this particle-swarm.

In the course of each year, the earth passes through a number of particle-swarms of varying densities. Some of the resulting meteor showers, like the Leonids and Giacobinids, are very feeble in most years, but sometimes produce spectacular displays.

The more important recognized meteor showers are:

NAME OF SHOWER	DATE OF MAXIMUM
Quadrantids	January 1-3
Lyrids	April 21
Eta-Aquarids	May 4-6
Perseids	August 10-14
Giacobinids (Nu-Draconids)	October 9
Orionids	October 20-23
Leonids	November 16-17
Geminids	December 12-13

Certain daytime streams are also known to be active during June and July. These daytime showers are, of course, invisible in the glare of sunlight, but they can be picked up by radar devices like those used in World War II to spot enemy airplanes.

Some meteor showers have been splendid enough to make a place for themselves in the historical record. Examples are the Leonid returns of 1833 and 1866, and the Giacobinid showers of 1933 and 1946. During these displays, meteors fell in a veritable fiery snowstorm, several hundred meteors sometimes appearing within a minute.

Not every annual return of a meteor shower is spectacular,

however, since conditions may not be favorable each year for a brilliant display. After all, both parties to a traffic collision at an intersection must try to pass through the intersection at the same time. Our earth, like a well-managed train, always goes through the intersection on schedule, but the particles responsible for meteor showers are much more erratic. They may be early or late—or they may not show up at all. Of the meteor showers seen annually, the Perseids are the most dependable. The Leonids put on their best shows at intervals of 33 years (1799-1800, 1832-33, 1866, etc.). The Giacobinids at intervals of 6½ years (1933, strong; 1939-40, poor; 1946, magnificent).

If you plan to observe a meteor shower, here are some suggestions. You will need:

Acquaintance with the stars, both faint and bright, in the region containing the radiant of the shower.

Comfortable reclining lawn-chair.

Warm clothing (including blankets) for winter showers or summer ones at high elevations.

A patient family that will not only approve of your observing but will help you get up to watch after midnight, when most showers are at their best.

A corner of your back yard (or sun roof) where you can shade your eyes from street lights and other illumination.

Timepiece, preferably with radiant dial.

Sit back and watch Nature put on her show. Any records you make may have some scientific value even if you note only these two things: Hourly number of meteors seen. Condition of the sky (clear, hazy, cloudy, etc.) during each hour of your watch.* At present, we know of only one instance in which it seems probable that a meteorite came to earth during a meteor shower. The Mazapil, Mexico, iron meteorite fell at 9:00 p.m. on November 27, 1885, during a return of the now very weak Bielid meteor shower. Scientists still cannot decide whether or not a mere coincidence was involved in this case.

As we have already mentioned, most of the cosmic particles rushing into our atmosphere evaporate and do not reach the earth at all except as the tiny congealed droplets and spherules of their own melt. Some cosmic particles, the *micro-meteorites,* are so tiny that they "stall" rather than fall down. These minute objects do not melt or disintegrate and so preserve their original cosmic form unchanged. Scientists have developed various methods for the collection of both of these types of material in order that at least rough estimates of their rate of accumulation on the earth can be made.

One of the simplest methods of collecting this so-called "meteoritic dust" is to expose a sticky glycerine-coated glass microscope slide for at least a 24-hour period in a protected spot well

* Readers who are advanced enough in astronomy to attempt plotting the meteor paths can get the proper star-maps and record sheets for this purpose by joining the American Meteor Society. Members must be at least 18 years old, but applicants between 14 and 18 can become probational members. For details write to Dr. C. P. Olivier, President, American Meteor Society, 521 North Wynnewood Avenue, Narberth, Pennsylvania.

away from locations where any industrial contamination is in the air. At the end of the period of exposure, the "catch" on the slide is examined microscopically, and the individual trapped particles are counted and classified. Meteoritic dust is also carried down to the ground by rain, snow, and hail and can therefore be obtained by filtering rainwater or melted glacier-ice, snow, and hail.

Such collection efforts have been plagued by the difficulty of identifying the particles. How can a collector be sure that the dust he has trapped, even though magnetic and possibly even in part metallic, does not come from some smelter or other industrial plant? Because of such uncertainties, the current estimates of the annual deposit of meteoritic dust for the world range from approximately 20 tons to several million tons. We need improved collection and identification techniques if we are to obtain trustworthy figures.

Recent analyses of rainfall records indicate that the infall of meteoritic dust produces at least one interesting weather-effect. These analyses show that rainfall peaks often occur some 30 days after the appearance of important meteor showers. Apparently, as meteoritic dust particles from the meteor showers filter down through the cloud systems in the lower layers of the atmosphere, the individual particles serve as centers about which atmospheric moisture condenses to form raindrops. The time lag of approximately a month is considered to be due to the very slow rate of fall of such tiny particles. It looks very much as if Mother Nature had beaten man to the idea of "seeding" the clouds to produce rainfall!

9. THE NATURE OF METE-ORITES

SO FAR in this book we have dealt with meteorites indirectly, chiefly in connection with their fall, distribution, and recovery. In this chapter, however, we are shifting our attention to the meteorites themselves, and will tell what the main types of meteorites are, what meteorites are made of, what they look like, and how to tell them from ordinary rocks.

First of all, meteorites neither all look alike nor have the same composition. The general term "meteorite" applies to any mass that reaches the earth from space. Such masses are made up of metals and minerals in varying proportions. The term "meteorite" is nearly as general in meaning as the word "rock," which geologists apply to bodies, large and small, that are formed by earth processes and are composed of various kinds of minerals. Actually, there are almost as many different kinds of meteorites as there are kinds of rocks; so you can see that in meteorites a wide range of composition and appearance is possible.

All recognized meteorites belong to one of three main divisions,* *irons, stones,* and *stony-irons.*

The irons are composed of an alloy of iron and nickel which may contain small inclusions of nonmetallic minerals.

After a cut section of an iron meteorite has been polished, the flat surface, except for possible inclusions, is mirror-like and re-

* Quite recently, a fourth division, the *tektites* (discussed in the next chapter), has been recognized by some authorities.

Internal structure revealed when the "etching" process is applied to that type of meteorite known as a "granular hexahedrite." See p. 120.

sembles stainless steel. It appears to be remarkably uniform and uninteresting, but this appearance is misleading. A characteristic and beautiful structural pattern develops when such a polished nickel-iron surface is treated with, for example, a special mixture of nitric acid, alcohol, and Arabol glue.

This process of treatment is known as "etching." The different structural patterns brought out by such etching give us the basis for classifying the iron meteorites.

If the etching process reveals certain features from which we can infer a cubic, or 6-faced, crystalline structure, we classify the iron meteorite as a *hexahedrite*.

If etching produces a certain special pattern from which we can infer an 8-faced, or octahedral, crystalline structure, we recognize the second subdivision of iron meteorites: the *octahedrites*. This remarkable pattern was discovered and first described by Alois von Widmanstätten, of Vienna, in 1808.

The third subdivision of iron meteorites consists of the "structureless" *ataxites*. (From the Greek for "without arrangement.") On an ataxite, etching brings out only a finely granular pattern with a stippled appearance.

The *stones* are composed chiefly of minerals that are combinations of various elements with silicon and oxygen—for example, olivine $(Mg, Fe)_2SiO_4$. Meteorites belonging to this division also contain combinations of elements with oxygen—such as magnesium oxide (MgO) and aluminum oxide (Al_2O_3). Usually, the stony groundmass contains scattered specks, grains, and thin veins of the same shiny nickel-iron alloy that makes up the iron meteorites almost in their entirety.

A. BREZINA & E. COHEN PHOTO

Widmanstätten pattern which emerges when the carefully polished
surface of that type of iron meteorite technically known as a "fine
octahedrite" is "etched."

The *stony-irons,* as the name indicates, are an "in-between" division. Some of the stony-irons, called *pallasites,* are sponge-like but rigid networks of nickel-iron alloy in which the smoothly rounded openings in the sponge enclose small gemlike masses of olivine. A cut and polished section of a pallasite showing round and oval gems of yellow-green olivine set in a silvery mesh of nickel-iron is a beautiful museum specimen indeed!

In the *silicate-siderites,* another type of stony-iron, a nickel-iron matrix is studded with angular fragments, shreds, and splinters of silicate minerals of all sizes. In the photograph, we can see that each of the various areas of the nickel-iron matrix (lighter in color) exhibits its own distinct crystallographic orientation, as is clearly indicated by the different Widmanstätten patterns.

Even a hasty comparison of polished sections of silicate-siderites and pallasites will leave no doubt that two quite distinct modes of formation were required to produce stony-irons of such different types.

Meteoritic nickel-iron has the following average chemical composition. To the nearest tenth, this alloy contains: Iron (Fe), 90.9%; nickel (Ni), 8.5%; cobalt (Co), 0.6%. This alloy gave scientists the key to the development of commercial stainless steels. It may also contain small amounts of phosphorous, sulfur, copper, chromium, and carbon.

The average chemical composition of stony meteoritic material is somewhat more complicated. To the nearest tenth, the "stones" contain: oxygen (O), 41.0%; silicon (Si), 21.0%; iron (Fe), 15.5%; magnesium (Mg), 14.3%; aluminum (Al),

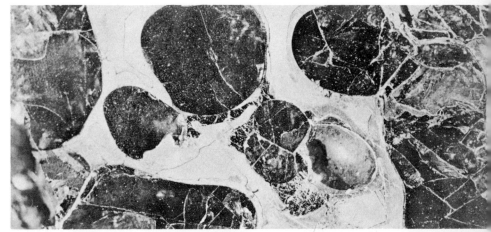

A. BREZINA & E. COHEN PHOTO

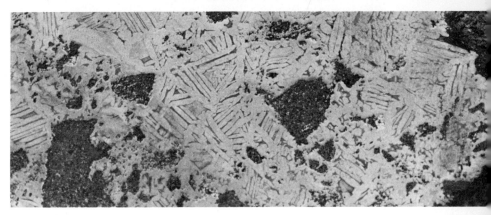

(above) Enlarged section of a stony-iron meteorite showing rounded olivine grains (dark in color) set in a network of nickel-iron alloy (light in color).

(below) Polished and etched section of a silicate-siderite showing angular fragments of silicate minerals (dark in color) imbedded in a metallic matrix.

1.6% ; calcium (Ca), 1.8% ; sulfur (S), 1.8%. The stony material may also contain smaller percentages of nickel, cobalt,
copper, carbon, chromium, and titanium.

In the stony-iron meteorites, we analyze the nickel-iron and
stony portions separately. On the average, each of these portions has about the chemical composition that is given for it
above.

Mineralogists have identified a variety of familiar minerals
in meteorites. These include olivine, the plagioclase feldspars,
magnetite, quartz, chromite, and, rarely, microscopic diamonds.
All of these minerals are found here on earth in such igneous
rocks as basalts and peridotites.

On the other hand, the meteoritic nickel-iron alloys (kama-
cite, taenite, and plessite, for example) and such meteoritic
minerals as schreibersite (nickel-iron phosphide) and daubree-
lite (iron chromium sulfide) do *not* occur naturally on the
earth.

We should stress here that although unusual *combinations*
of known elements are present in meteorites, no new *elements*
have been discovered during the increasingly intensive study of
these masses during the last 150 years.

The majority of stony meteorites show a structure not found
in terrestrial rocks. These meteorites are made up of rounded,
shot-like bodies called *chondrules* (from the Greek word for
"grain"). The individual chondrules may vary in size from
those as large or even larger than a walnut down to dust-sized
grains. The most common size is about that of peppercorns. The
chondrules are often composed of the same material as the

COURTESY OF AMERICAN MUSEUM OF NATURAL HISTORY

Microphotograph of a thin section of a chondrite, showing the circular, or nearly circular, cross sections of a number of chondrules, including one of large size at the upper edge of the section.

groundmass in which they are imbedded and unless the meteorite containing them is a very fragile one, they will break with the rest of the mass, as will sand grains in a quartzite. If the meteorite is fragile, however, the individual chondrules can generally be broken out whole. Meteorites containing chondrules are called *chondrites*.

A small percentage of stony meteorites have no chondrules. These meteorites are known as *achondrites* (meaning "not chondrites") and they resemble terrestrial rocks more closely than the chondrites do. Some achondrites contain almost no trace whatever of metal, although in others (for example, the Norton County meteorite, of Chapter 2) small lumps and specks of nickel-iron are sparsely distributed through the stony groundmass.

Meteorites are as variable in shape as they are in composition and structure. Many are cone-shaped; others shield-, bell-, or ring-shaped; still others pear-shaped. One iron fragment recently recovered from the Glorieta, New Mexico, fall has been described as "macro-spicular," meaning needle-shaped on a very large scale. The photographs opposite illustrate a number of the commoner forms known. The Glorieta specimen has been nicknamed "Alley Oop's shillelagh," for only a person of great strength could wield this 13-pounder with ease!

In general, the shape of meteorites depends upon the amount of mass lost by "evaporation" during passage through the earth's atmosphere. This factor, in turn, depends not only upon the speed of transit, but also on such physical characteristics of the meteorite as its tensile strength and whether or not it con-

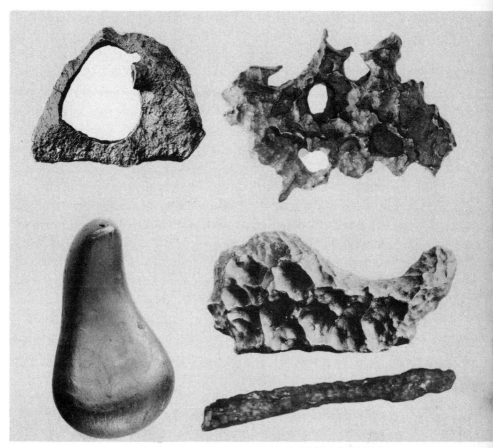

CHICAGO MUSEUM OF NATURAL HISTORY PHOTOS
(BOTTOM RIGHT) INSTITUTE OF METEORITICS PHOTO

A few of the many shapes exhibited by meteorites: ring-shaped, perforated and highly irregular, pear-shaped, jaw shaped, needle-shaped.

tains certain alloys and minerals that vaporize more easily than the rest of the meteorite. The ring-shape of the Tucson, Arizona, iron is believed to have resulted from the "melting away" of a huge inclusion of stony material during the descent of the meteorite.

When meteorites are recovered and taken to the laboratory for study, one of the first things scientists do is to weigh them. If a meteorite is very large, special scales sometimes have to be constructed for this purpose. Such was the case for the largest meteorite so far weighed: the giant Ahnighito, Greenland, meteorite, which Peary brought to New York City by ship. (See Chapter 3.) A specially constructed scale on which this huge mass is now mounted gives for its weight about 68,000 pounds. Other meteorites famous for their great size are: the Bacubirito, Mexico, 27 tons; Willamette, Oregon, 14 tons; Morito, Mexico, 11 tons; and the Bendego, Brazil, 5 tons. All of these are irons.

The largest stone meteorite so far recovered as one mass is the so-called Furnas County, Nebraska, stone, which is the principal fragment of the Norton, Kansas, fall, and weighs about 2,360 pounds.

At the other end of the size-range, investigators have recovered meteoritic masses weighing no more than a small fraction of a gram. From a stone shower that occurred at Holbrook, Arizona, field searchers have found some of the very smallest specimens in anthills. The insects had carried these tiny meteorites along with sand and garnet grains in building their hills!

COURTESY OF AMERICAN MUSEUM OF NATURAL HISTORY

The Willamette iron, famous for its great size and weight (14 tons), on exhibit at the Hayden Planetarium, New York City. See pp. 36, 39.

The only sure way to determine whether or not an object *is* a meteorite is to have a small piece of it (say, a fragment the size of an egg) tested chemically and microscopically by an expert on meteorites. Nevertheless, there are several questions whose answers will help you to decide whether or not you are on the right track in suspecting that a "rock" you have found may be a meteorite:

> Is your specimen especially heavy?
>
> Does your specimen show a thin blackish or brownish crust on its outer surface?
>
> Does your "rock" have shallow, oval pits on its outer surface?
>
> If the specimen has a corner knocked off, do you see specks and grains of metal on the broken surface?

Is your specimen especially heavy? The iron and stony-iron meteorites are very heavy. A 1-inch cube of iron meteorite weighs approximately 8 times as much as a 1-inch cube of ice. Even the stones, which are only about half as dense as the irons, are much heavier than ordinary rocks.

Does your specimen show a thin blackish or brownish crust on its outer surfaces? You will recall that specimens of both the Ussuri and Norton meteorites showed a "glaze" of fused material which we call fusion crust. Most freshly-fallen meteorites are covered with such a crust. To illustrate how this crust forms, consider a snowball that you bravely hold in your freezing hand until the outer surface melts. If you then were to leave

Piezoglyphs (oval pits resembling thumb-prints) in a stone meteorite, found at Belly River, Canada. See p. 132.

the snowball outside overnight, the melted outer surface would freeze into a hard crust.

In similar fashion, the surface of a meteorite melts during the blazing-hot part of its flight through the air, only to "freeze" into a hard, firm coating in the lower, cooler portions of its path. This hardened coating, the fusion crust, is of much importance. Its presence is one of the best indications that a "rock" is really a meteorite. From the character of the fusion crust, experts can piece together a good deal about what happened to a meteorite on its way down to earth. If you should be lucky enough to find a meteorite, don't break off the fusion crust. A whole encrusted specimen in the hand is worth 200 crustless fragments scattered at your feet!

Does your "rock" have shallow, oval pits or depressions on its outer surface? Such features are known technically as *piezoglyphs* (Greek *piezein,* to press + *glyph,* to carve) and popularly as "thumb-prints." They were formed during the meteorite's flight through the atmosphere when the softer portions of its outer shell were "eroded" away, leaving small scooped-out places. These pittings are very similar to the prints that would be made by the human hand in a lump of modeling clay or bread dough. In one case, they gave rise to the false idea that the meteorite had fallen in a plastic state and that the imprints had been formed when its finders first pulled the mass out of the ground by hand.

If the specimen you have found already has a corner knocked off, do you see specks and grains of metal on the broken surface? Such scattered bits of nickel-iron (not to be confused with the shiny mica flakes often seen in igneous rocks) character-istically occur in the grayish or brownish groundmass of stony meteorites. If your specimen is unbroken, hold it lightly against a spinning carborundum wheel or use a file to grind a small flat surface upon it, and then examine this surface for specks of metal.

If the answers to these questions are yes, then there is a good possibility that you have found a genuine meteorite.

If meteorites remain buried in the ground for a long period of time, their characteristic surface-features may weather away. Under such conditions, iron meteorites develop heavy-layered coatings of rust (iron oxide) as much as several inches in thick-ness. If irons stay in the ground long enough, they may rust away almost completely and turn into shale balls, like those found near the ancient Wolf Creek, Australia meteorite crater. (See Chapter 4.) Stone meteories buried in the ground for any great length of time may disintegrate and become completely unrecognizable as meteorites.

The fact that meteorites of all kinds are attacked by weather-ing has always argued strongly in favor of their prompt recovery. In the case of witnessed falls, prompt recovery is even more important, for only thus can specimens still retaining measurable amounts of various short-lived radioactivities be made avail-able to physicists eager to investigate them with the most modern radiometric equipment.

10. TEKTITES, IMPACTITES & "FOSSIL" METEORITES

BEFORE southern Australia was occupied by the white man, the native tribesmen of that region treasured certain small rounded pieces of black glass as medicine stones, rainmaking stones, and message stones. The Wadikali tribe referred to these objects as *mindjimindjilpara,* a word meaning "eyes that look at you like a man staring hard." The early European settlers of the area called the same black glassy masses "blackfellows' buttons." Both phrases applied to objects that modern scientists call "australites," which are now one of the best known types of *tektites* (Greek: *tēktos,* molten).

These Australian tektites and the tektites from many other countries around the world are a problem to meteoriticists. The question is, are they really meteorites? Many investigators believe that the answer is yes, and they are inclined to add to the three main divisions of true meteorites listed in the preceding chapter, a fourth: the tektites.

These mysterious glassy objects occur in such widely separated localities as Czechoslovakia, the Philippine Islands, Borneo, the Ivory Coast of Africa, Australia, Indo-China, Texas, Malaya, and Java. In these and still other areas, they have been found by the thousands in surface deposits of sand, clay, and gravel.

Tektites have never been seen to fall. In spite of this fact, as we noted above, a number of scientists believe that, like the

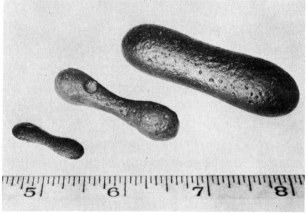

(left) "Flanged buttons" from Australia. (right) Several sizes of "dumbbells" from Australia. See p. 136.

meteorites, the tektites really did come from outer space but, that they fell to earth before man was here to see them come down—or at least before he had acquired the means and skill to make lasting records of such an occurrence.

Tektites are usually quite small, weighing between 1 and 100 grams, although a few of much larger size have been found. One large specimen from the Philippines weighed about ½ pound. Two giant tektites, one weighing ¾ pound and the other over 1 pound, are in the collection of the British Museum. In composition, tektites are an impure silica-glass containing low percentages of the oxides of such elements as iron, magnesium, calcium, and titanium.

If tektite fragments are held under a lamp and observed by reflected light, their thicker parts generally appear to be jet-black. If, however, these same specimens are held up *between* the observer and the light, then their thin razor-sharp edges are seen to be bottle-green, yellow-green, brownish, or even color-less.

In shape, many tektites are roundish or oval. Others are shaped like dumbbells, ladles, canoes, and teardrops. So they are known by those descriptive terms. One particularly inter-esting example is the unusual "flanged button" of Australia. Tektites of this type look like miniature South American gold-pans, the *bateas*, heaped high with pay dirt. Australian gold-field workers regarded these tektites as magical, and used them as good-luck charms. Superstitious American gold-seekers brought them into the United States all the way from Australia!

Some tektites (for example, many of the "bediasites" from

(above) Rounded tektite from Texas. (below) Deeply grooved bedi-asite from Texas.

Texas) are deeply grooved and channeled, and have a very jagged and irregular appearance. Even the smoother tektite surfaces are characterized by flow lines, flow ridges, and bubble pits.

Many weathered pebbles and fragments of obsidian somewhat resemble the tektites superficially. There is a very simple test by which you can distinguish true tektites from obsidian. If you hold a thin splinter of tektite glass in a blowpipe flame, the glass melts quietly but only with the greatest difficulty. On the contrary, when you test in the same flame the terrestrial glass, obsidian, it froths up much more easily, into a bubbly, whitish mass.

Although the question of where the tektites came from is still not entirely settled, most scientists agree that all tektites did have a *common* origin. For example, tektites from widely scattered localities on the earth's surface show not only similar queer shapes and surface markings (technically known as "sculpturing"), but also have very much the same chemical composition and, in particular, the same content of radioactive elements.

Because the tektites chemically resemble certain terrestrial rocks, scientists at first believed that some kind of earth process must have created them. One suggestion was that lightning had fused dust particles suspended in the air to form them; another, that they had come from volcanoes; still another, that the tektites were simply inclusions that had weathered out of terrestrial rocks. A few scientists once took seriously the possibility that tektites were refuse from primitive glass factories!

While such theories have not yet been completely discarded, most scientists now feel that the tektites had their origin some-

Tektite vs. obsidian, after blowpipe test.

where outside the earth. There are several reasons for this belief. First, the shape of such unusually symmetrical forms as are found, for example, among the australites, indicates that these small bodies at one time were members of a swarm of freely-spinning liquid masses. Again, flow features observed on the surfaces of certain tektites (and the fusion crust definitely identified on one specimen) show that these bodies at some time must have traveled through the earth's atmosphere at high velocity.

If, then, the tektites were not produced by earth processes, where did they come from? According to primitive legends, they were "rocks" or "pebbles" from the moon. Indeed, one of the earliest scientific theories as to their origin (proposed by the Dutch authority Verbeek in 1897) likewise attributes them to debris jetted out from the moon. Another holds that tektites are fragments of the outermost glassy layers of some so-called "meteorite-planet," or planets.* Still another idea is that tektites are what is left of a comet when it passes so close to the blazing-hot sun that the "ices" which make up most of the cometary nucleus (head) are all distilled away.

These theories of the origin of the tektites are based primarily on their observed shapes, surface features, and compositions. The senior author of this book has suggested still another possible theory based on the very unusual nature of the observed distribution of the tektites on the face of the earth.

To explain this theory, we first recall that the planet on which we live is more nearly a true sphere than are such familiar

* Discussed in Chapter 12.

Every plane passing through the center of a sphere intersects the surface in a great circle. In this figure, only the front half of the great circle cut out by the plane is shown.

"spherical" objects as baseballs or basketballs. Consequently, any plane through the center of the earth cuts its surface in a curve that to all intents and purposes is what geometers refer to as a *great circle*.

Now the significant fact is that all the tektite deposits known at present are located on or very near to three great circles on the earth's surface. Mathematics shows that if some earth process had created the tektites at random over the surface of the earth, then the odds would be very strongly against the existence of this peculiar "great-circle distribution." But such distribution along great circles would be *expected* if the tektites had resulted from what might be likened to "chain-falls" upon the earth of objects like nearby satellites moving in orbits encircling our globe.

This notion brings up the interesting possibility that at some time in the remote past, the earth may have been the proud possessor of a set of equatorial rings. These rings would have been similar to those at present circling in the plane of Saturn's equator. (Jupiter, too, may once have had its own set of equatorial rings.) The rings of Saturn are known to be made up of countless very small meteorites. In the same way, the "earth rings" of prehistory could have consisted of swarms of tiny nearby meteoritic satellites—the tektites—moving about the earth in the plane of its then-existing equator.

Eventually, the innermost of these small natural satellites collapsed onto the earth's surface, falling along the old equator. At least twice thereafter, this process was repeated, the points of impact of the later tektite falls again lining up along whatever great circle of the earth happened to be the equator at the time of fall.

As the geologists and other investigators have shown, major shifts have occurred in the position of the earth's equator during past geologic ages. This fact is well-substantiated by discoveries of fossil shells and plants on the cold Antarctic continent and of glacial deposits in hot South Africa. Therefore, we could hardly expect the tektite deposits, which are believed to have fallen at widely separated intervals of time, to have all occurred along a *single* great circle on the earth's surface.

As you can see, the so-called "tektite-puzzle" is a complex one. As if this were not bad enough, Mother Nature has added to the confusion by creating in addition to the tektites another type of silica-glass not only found along the very same three great circles sprinkled with true tektites, but also having other features in common with the tektite glasses.

At Mount Darwin in Tasmania and at Wabar in the Rub' al Khali desert of Arabia, large and small fragments of this curious silica-glass have been collected. At Wabar the masses of silica-glass were found in and about the rims of a series of meteorite craters formed in nearly pure sand, as we pointed out in Chapter 4. These meteorite craters are known to have resulted from the high-speed impact of iron meteorites upon the sand dunes of the Wabar site. Since the silica-glasses of Wabar have been found to contain countless spherules of nickel-iron of the same composition as the iron meteorites discovered about the Wabar meteorite craters, it seems quite certain that both the sand of the earth target and the nickel-iron of the falling meteorites were vaporized by the intense heat generated at impact. Consequently, it is natural that these Wabar masses of congealed silica-glass and nickel-iron be called *impactites*. They are silica-glasses, created chiefly from *terrestrial* materials by the impact of large crater-forming meteorites. This same name is now applied to all silica-glasses believed to have the same origin as those at Wabar.

As regards size if not composition, the crater-forming meteorites responsible for the Wabar and other impactites may have been big brothers of the small-fry responsible for the showers of true tektites. Or these big ones may have moved about the earth in orbits distinct from those followed by the tektite swarms but lying in the same plane as one of these swarms.

In addition to the curious puzzle of the tektites, meteoriticists have also run up against the problem of "fossil" meteorites or, more exactly, the problem of the *lack* of "fossil" meteorites. As we have already mentioned, no positively identified meteorite has ever been found in other than the most recent rock layers. With all the mining—particularly coal mining—that has gone on throughout the world in historic times, this fact does seem astonishing.

A number of explanations can be suggested for this absence of ancient meteorites. In the geologic past, meteorite falls may not have occurred as often as they do today. For example, the primeval atmosphere of the earth may have been so much denser than at present that even quite large meteorites were totally vaporized as they passed through it and therefore never reached the ground. Again, even if the rate of infall of meteorites was the same in the remote past as now, still various weathering processes active ever since the earliest meteorites fell may have so changed them in appearance and composition that they are no longer recognizable for what they are.

Several unusual lumps of rock from England and a mass of iron from Austria, all found at some depth by coal miners, have been tentatively put forward as "fossil" meteorites. But studies of these masses have so far produced no conclusive re-

L. J. SPENCER PHOTO
COURTESY OF AMERICAN MUSEUM OF NATURAL HISTORY

Mysterious glass objects found in the Libyan Desert. (right) Cut and polished specimens.

sults. Still, we should not ignore the possibility that someday meteorites may be found and identified in rocks of considerable age.

Does it seem as if we have posed more problems than we have solved in this chapter? It is very true that we have done just that. In speaking briefly about the tektites, the impactites, and the absence of "fossil" meteorites, we have by no means tried to present the last word on the troublesome but highly interesting problems connected with these objects—problems that admittedly may take scientists years or even decades of further research to solve. Perhaps you will find here the kind of unusual and thought-provoking problems that make the study of meteorites a rather special challenge. If so, you may wish to take an active part someday in unraveling these puzzles.

11. OMENS AND FANTASIES

MEN SEEM to have always taken an interest in meteorites, but not until the early nineteenth century were these objects considered to be worth preserving for *scientific* study.

In the beginning, people believed that because meteorites fell from the heavens, they were either gods themselves or messengers from the gods. The more civilized of early men therefore carefully kept the fallen meteorites. They draped them in costly linens and anointed them with oil. In many instances, the people built special temples in which meteorites were actually worshipped. Some of the holy stones of the ancients, such as the Diana of the Ephesians, mentioned in the Bible as "the image which fell down from Jupiter,"* are now thought to have been meteorites.

Meteorite worship was common long ago in the Mediterranean area and in Africa, India, Japan, and Mexico. This practice still persists in some regions even in modern times. The Black Stone of the Kaaba, for example, has been sacred to all Mohammedans from about 700 A.D. right up to the present. It is said to be a meteorite although this fact has never been verified, because strict religious taboos connected with the stone prevent any scientific examination or study of it. On the contrary, the Andhâra, India, meteorite is known to be a genuine one. The story of the fall and preservation of this meteorite provides a fairly modern example of practices rooted in the ritual and custom of far more ancient times.

* The Acts of the Apostles, 19:35.

At about 4:00 in the afternoon of December 2, 1880, the people of Andhâra heard a noise like that made by a gun. Some of the villagers saw a "dark ball" come to earth in a field near them. This falling object sent up a small cloud of dust as it struck the ground. After the stone had been recovered from the field and the dust had been washed from its surface, two Brahmin priests took charge of it and began to collect money for the erection of a temple in which the holy object could be properly displayed.

The scientist who promptly investigated the Andhâra fall reported that throngs of worshippers were crowding into the as yet unfinished brick temple to make offerings of flowers, sweetmeats, milk, rice, water, bel leaves, and of course money. The stone had been named Adbhuta-Nâth, "the miraculous god." It was shaped like a round loaf of blackish bread and weighed an estimated 6 pounds. The scientist was not allowed to touch it, but he got close enough to verify that the stone was a meteorite covered with a typical blackish fusion crust.

Not only has man worshipped meteorites, but during a period extending from approximately 300 B.C. to 300 A.D., emperors and self-governing cities frequently marked the fall of meteorites by minting special coins or medals known as *betyls*.* One of these is the betyl of Emisa, Syria, made by Antonius Pius (138-161 A.D.). The historian, Herodotus, accurately described the object honored by this betyl as: "A large stone, which on the lower side is round, and above runs gradually to a point. It has

* Also *baetyl* and *baetulus,* from the Greek word *baitylos,* a term used for sacred meteorites and stones.

COURTESY OF AMERICAN MUSEUM OF NATURAL HISTORY

Drawing of multiple fireball, over Athens, October 18, 1863. J. F. J.
Schmidt, the celebrated pioneer fireball observer, described it as a
mass of dazzling light "bringing into view land and sea, with the
Acropolis and the Parthenon a mile away across the city."

Oceanside Public Library

nearly the form of a cone, and is of a black color. *People say of it in earnest that it fell from Heaven."* The stone is shown on the coin as carried on a quadriga (a carriage drawn by four horses) under a canopy of four sunshades.

Many ancient peoples held meteorites in great reverence, particularly if they were seen to fall. But at the same time, other more practical-minded individuals made good use of the durable and easily worked alloy provided by nature in the nickel-iron meteorites. This alloy was frequently used to make ax-heads, spear and harpoon points, knives, farming tools, stirrups and spurs, and even pots and other utensils. Archeologists have found earrings and similar ornaments overlaid with thin sheets of hammered meteoritic iron in Indian mounds of the Ohio Valley. They have also discovered round beads made of nickel-iron in Indian mounds of the Havana, Illinois, area and in the still more ancient Egyptian ruins at Gerzah.

Meteoritic iron has often been used in the manufacture of special swords, daggers, and knives for members of the royalty. Atilla and other early conquerors of Europe boasted of "swords from heaven." Emperor Jehangir (1605-1627) ordered two sword blades, a knife, and a dagger to be smelted from the Jalandhar, India, meteorite, which fell on April 10, 1621. In the early nineteenth century, a sword was manufactured from a portion of the Cape of Good Hope meteorite for presentation to Alexander, the Emperor of Russia. Even as late as the end of the nineteenth century, several swords were made from a part of the Shirihagi, Japan, iron meteorite at the command of a member of the Japanese court.

A Russian artist's pen-and-ink drawing of an extremely brilliant
detonating fire ball or bolide. See page 102.

In the Europe of the Middle Ages, meteorite falls and meteor showers, as well as other "unnatural" events like comets, eclipses, and displays of the aurora borealis, were regarded with superstitious awe by commoner and king alike. The medieval mind always sought to interpret events connected in any way with the heavens as somehow influencing the affairs of men. A bishop explained that the great meteor shower of April 4, 1095, forecast "the changes and wanderings of nations from kingdom to kingdom." The fact, however, that the First Crusade began within a year, is mere coincidence.

In referring to celestial events, Shakespeare often expressed the view that was common in the Middle Ages and the Renaissance. An example is:

> The bay-trees in our country are all wither'd
> And meteors fright the fixed stars of heaven;
> The pale-faced moon looks bloody on the earth
> And lean-look'd prophets whisper fearful change,
>
> . . . . .
> These signs forerun the death or fall of kings.
>
> (*Richard II*, II, iv, 8-11, 15)

Yet the descent of meteorites from the heavens was not always regarded as a forewarning of bad fortune. On November 16, 1492, a 279-pound meteorite fell at Ensisheim in Alsace, not far from the battle line separating the armies of France and the Holy Roman Empire. Emperor Maximilian, the leader of the Empire's forces, commanded that the fallen stone be carried to his castle. There a formal war-council was held to determine what the strange event could mean.

The Emperor and his councillors decided that the fall of the meteorite at such a time and place was an omen of divine favor

COURTESY OF AMERICAN MUSEUM OF NATURAL HISTORY

Drawing of Andromedid meteor shower, November 27, 1872.

which meant good fortune to the cause of the Holy Roman Empire. After breaking off two small pieces of the stone, one for the Duke of Austria and one for himself, the Emperor forbade further damage to it. He also gave orders that the stone be hung in the parish church in Ensisheim for all to see. In this way, the Ensisheim stone became the very first meteorite of witnessed fall to be preserved down to the present day—and all because of the superstition of a famous military leader.

The discussion to this point makes clear that in ancient, medieval, and Renaissance times, meteorite falls were considered as startling and disturbing events, which frequently were interpreted in strange and mistaken ways. But the fact that meteorites actually did fall from the heavens was not questioned. As the so-called "Age of Reason" opened, a curious change in attitude toward meteorite falls took place.

At the very time that knowledge in general increased, men of learning began to deny that meteorite falls occurred at all! The scientists of the French Academy, in particular, were very positive on this point. Since the era was one in which all Europe sneezed if "la belle France" had a cold in the head, it was a trying time not only for the early meteoriticists, but for all who had the nerve to insist they had seen rocks fall from the sky.

By the end of the 1700's, the authorities had studied the evidence relating to meteorite falls and had completely rejected it. They said that there was no "proof" whatever that "stones fell from the heavens." These early scientists openly sneered at people who claimed that they had seen meteorites fall. It was felt that the spectators of such events either had merely been

Oceanside Public Library

"seeing things," or had surely been reporting light and sound effects connected with nothing but ordinary thunderstorms.

When confronted with the "fallen" masses themselves, the authorities often refused to examine them, or if they did, insisted that these masses were only rocks that had been struck by lightning. Such were the opinions of learned men around the close of the eighteenth century.

Fortunately, scientific facts have a stubborn way of winning out in the long run. A major part of the credit for seeing that the truth regarding meteorite falls was at last recognized must go to E. F. F. Chladni, a German physicist, and to Edward Howard, an English chemist.

In 1794, Chladni published an extremely important paper concerning a large spongelike mass of "native iron" found near Krasnoyarsk, Russia. This object had been discovered in 1749 by a Russian blacksmith, and it was studied in 1772 by P. S. Pallas, an early traveler. Chladni concluded that the mass of iron* must have fallen from the heavens, because it had been "fused" (but not by man, electricity, or fire) and also because there were no volcanoes anywhere around its place of find.

Chladni supported his theory by listing numerous reports of meteorite falls dating from ancient and medieval times. But Chladni's fellow scientists flatly rejected his theory as clever but not satisfactory.

With the fall of the Siena meteorites in Italy on June 16, 1794,

---

* This metallic mass was the first stony-iron meteorite to be identified as such. The *pallasites,* which make up an important subdivision of the stony-iron meteorites, were named in honor of Pallas.

the controversy regarding the possibility that stones actually fell from the sky became particularly heated, and remained so for nearly ten years. During this interval, two other important meteorite falls occurred: Wold Cottage, England, on December 13, 1795, and Benares, India, on December 19, 1798. Scientists had a hard time finding explanations for these well-observed events, and some of the theories put forward to account for them far outdid Chladni's in "cleverness," if that be the correct word.

One scholar, writing in 1796, suggested that the masses which fell at Siena resulted from the solidification at great height of volcanic ashes from Mount Vesuvius. These ashes had supposedly been carried northward beyond Siena and then been "brought back by a northerly wind, congealing from the air . . ."

Fortunately, in 1803 Edward Howard's chemical work on meteorites came to a successful conclusion. This patient chemist made analyses of samples from the Siena, Wold Cottage, and Benares falls and from an older Bohemian fall. He also had the samples studied mineralogically by a fellow scientist. From the results of these investigations, he drew the following conclusions, which admirably supported Chladni's well-reasoned and thoroughly documented theory regarding meteorite falls:

All four of the stones studied had very nearly the same composition.

Despite the fact that the stones contained no new elements, their mineralogical character differed in several important respects from that of any rocks found naturally on the earth.

The four masses must have had a common origin although their reported falls had been widely separated both in time and in space.

Finally, said Howard, it was quite possible that the stones had really fallen from the sky.

Howard's views were soon put to the test. Shortly after the publication of his important paper, a shower of stony meteorites fell near L'Aigle, France, on April 26, 1803. This event was carefully investigated by French scientists, and they reluctantly admitted that about 3,000 stones actually had fallen within an oval-shaped area about 6 miles long by 2 miles wide. This shower of meteorites had been accompanied by the same light and sound effects mentioned in many of the old meteorite-fall reports collected by Chladni, effects now recognized as characteristic of the infall of meteorites upon the earth. The evidence was overwhelming—stones really did fall from the sky. In the camp of the enemy, so to speak, the reality of meteorite falls was established once and for all!

12. THE MODERN VIEW

AFTER THE L'Aigle shower of 1803, a whole new era opened in the study of meteorites. No longer did scientists hold these objects up to ridicule and scorn. Instead, they came to regard meteorites as well worth collection and careful study.

The Vienna Museum, the British Museum, the Paris Museum, the Academy of Science of St. Petersburg (now Leningrad), and the U.S. National Museum began to build up splendid meteorite collections. Scientists in Germany, England, France, and Russia engaged in the painstaking mineralogical study and classification of individual meteorite specimens.

The modern science of meteoritics is rooted deep in the nineteenth century. Many special fields of investigation had their beginnings then. Scientists became interested in the chemistry, the mineralogy, and the metallurgy of meteorites; in the orbits of meteorites and the trajectories they follow through the earth's atmosphere down to impact with the ground; and in the distribution of meteorite falls in space and time.

From this period we can date such milestones of progress in meteoritics as:

The discovery of the beautiful and significant Widmanstätten patterns characteristic of the majority of the irons, and the less spectacular but equally important lines named for J. G. Neumann, the German meteoriticist who discovered them, in 1848, in the Braunau meteorite.

The realization that there were many different kinds of meteor-

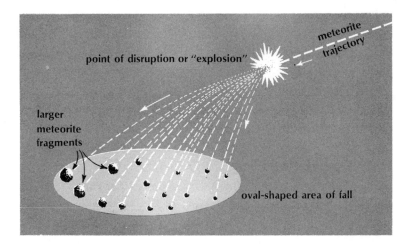

Typical distribution of meteorite fragments according to size, within oval-shaped area of fall. The larger masses of the shower carry farther on, in the direction of the motion of the meteorite. As early as 1814, investigators had noted this peculiarity of meteorite-shower distributions. See pp. 32, 89, 94.

ites and that these diverse objects were very important to an understanding of the internal structure and origin of the earth, and perhaps of the Solar System and the wider cosmos as well.

Tentative explanations of the violent and terrifying light and sound effects connected with meteorite falls.

Tentative explanations of such oval-shaped areas as shown above.

By 1850, A. Boisse, an early French geologist and meteoriticist, had put forth the basic *meteorite-planet* hypothesis. According to this theory of his, meteorites are the fragments of a planet*
that formerly orbited between Mars and Jupiter in what is now
called the "asteroid belt." And untold millions of years ago,
this planet was shattered by some unknown but very great force,
possibly collision with another celestial body.

The structure of the meteorite-planet was considered to have
been very much like that of the earth. The various divisions of
recognized meteorites were believed to be representatives of
the several concentric, or nested, shells of material originally
making up the destroyed planet. These shells were progressively
less dense with increasing distance from the center of the planet.

Today Boisse's theory is one of the most widely accepted as
an explanation of at least one major category of the meteorites.
Some modern investigators would insist that the meteorite-
planet had a thin outer glassy shell from which the tektites came.

Most of the larger fragments of the meteorite-planet, now
called the *asteroids,* move so that the average asteroidal orbit
very closely approximates the orbit of the original planet. But
many of the smaller fragments follow paths in space that differ
considerably from the original meteorite-planet's orbit. Even
some of the asteroids behave this way, either because of the high
speeds they acquired at the time of disruption of the meteorite-
planet, or because of the later influence of the major planets and
particularly of the giant planet, Jupiter.

* Very recently, some authorities have concluded that there must have been
not one but several meteorite-planets.

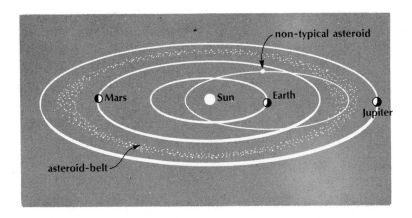

A diagram (not drawn to scale) showing position of asteroid-belt with respect to the orbits of Mars and Jupiter. The asteroids with average orbits move within this belt. The non-typical asteroid indicated follows an orbit that brings it well inside that of the earth. There are a number of asteroids with such peculiar orbits. It is possible that in the past a nickel-iron asteroid in one of these orbits collided with the earth and produced the Canyon Diablo meteorite crater.

In fact, at the present time, several asteroids move well within the orbits of the earth and Venus. It is quite possible therefore that such a large meteorite crater as the one at Canyon Diablo, was produced by the prehistoric fall of one of these small members of our Solar System. If so, we have reason to believe that a core-fragment of the meteorite-planet came to earth at Canyon Diablo. For the extensive mining operations carried out there during the last half-century have shown that the projectile responsible for this greatest of all meteoritic shell-holes in the face of Mother Earth was a mass of solid nickel-iron, which in all likelihood was core material.

The lengthy and costly series of mining operations at Canyon Diablo were all undertaken in the hope of locating the "main mass" of this huge projectile and thus of opening up what might be called a cosmic-lode of quite valuable metals. Unfortunately, the miners overlooked the fact that impacts at meteoritic speeds produced almost incredible amounts of heat. Even the solid iron meteorites are vaporized and widely dispersed at the temperatures resulting from such impacts, as we have seen was the case at Wabar (see Chapter 4). So it was at Canyon Diablo.

The idea of a cosmic-metal mine might at first strike some readers as too futuristic to take seriously. But the necessity for catching a core-fragment before it enters the consuming atmosphere of our planet is really nothing new. As far back as 1939, the senior author had occasion to point out that if we wish to start a successful cosmic-metal mine, we must catch our core-fragment before it is turned into unminable vapor. This point will come up again in the next chapter.

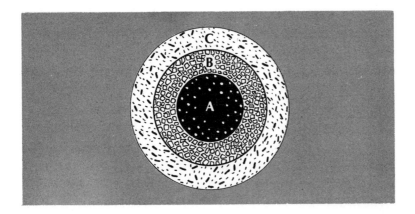

Cross-section of Boisse's hypothetical meteorite-planet. Fragmentation of this sphere was believed to have given rise to the following divisions of meteorites:

The *iron* meteorites came from **A,** the dense nickel-iron core.

The stony-iron meteorites came from **B**, the intermediate zone of cellular nickel-iron and silicate minerals.

The *stony* meteorites came from **C,** the outer zone of silicate minerals in which relatively little or no nickel-iron is present. The chondrites were believed to come from the inner portion of this zone; the achondrites, from the outer portion.

There are several other theories of the origin of meteorites interesting enough to mention. The early view that the meteorites were debris thrown out by ancient volcanoes on the moon or recent ones on the earth came to be discredited largely on physical grounds. On the other hand, extremely violent *primordial* volcanoes on the earth (not the weak ones of historic times, like Aetna or Vesuvius) could have ejected material that in much later times fell, and continues to fall back on our globe. This theory has not been ruled out and it still receives support, for example, from some authorities in the U.S.S.R. These same Russian scientists take most seriously a suggestion that the meteorites (and comets as well) were thrown out by volcanoes believed to exist on the planet, Jupiter—a theory dating back almost a century to the English astronomer, R. A. Proctor.

Some scientists believe that meteorites represent the congealed remains of gaseous bolts of matter ejected by the sun. Others interpret them as fragments of comets that have been torn apart by passing too close to the sun, which is the most powerful gravitational center in the Solar System.

Chemists, geologists, astronomers, and physicists—as well as the meteoriticists themselves—are constantly working toward a solution of the problem of the meteorites. Where do these bodies come from? What can we learn from them about their age and origin and about the age and origin of our Solar System? Years may be required, but eventually the riddle of the meteorites will be solved by the patient, concerted efforts of men and women of science.

Collapsed mine buildings in the bottom of the Canyon Diablo meteorite crater. A shaft was put down here in one of several unsuccessful attempts to locate the main mass of the meteorite. See pp.
44-52.

13. PRESENT AND FUTURE APPLICATIONS

S O F A R we have considered what might be called the "pure" rather than the "applied" side of the study of meteorites. The investigator in any pure science asks of a new discovery, "What does this tell me about the universe? How does it better help me to understand the laws of nature?" Of the same discovery, however, the worker in an applied science will ask, "What practical use can be made of this gain in knowledge? What can it be made to do for mankind in general?"

These questions reveal a decided difference in viewpoint, but this difference does not reflect unfavorably on either class of scientists. In fact, there is a great deal of truth in the saying "Today's pure science is tomorrow's applied." Actually, ways and means of taking advantage of seemingly useless scientific discoveries are constantly being found. The most famous example of this principle is the development of the atomic bomb from the results of Einstein's researches in the abstract field of relativity. Here the seemingly mystic formula $E = mc^2$ came to have far-reaching practical applications indeed!

Meteoritics has some exceedingly practical applications. Far from being completely "out of this world"—as the recovered meteorites themselves originally were—this science has been and can be made to serve mankind in a number of rather unexpected ways. Meteoritics, the onetime "stepchild of astronomy," is currently being regarded with ever-increasing respect by scientists and engineers working in many different fields.

Consider, first of all, the stainless steels that are so widely used in modern industry, and even the fine satin-sheen stainless "silverware" that graces our dining tables. These have wisely been patterned after a natural alloy with lasting qualities of strength, tenacity, and resistance to corrosion. This natural alloy is the one making up the iron meteorites.

Its toughness and durability became well known wherever attempts were made to section these metallic meteorites. Specially designed and extra-powerful sawing equipment is required to slice meteoritic iron, and even with it, progress is painfully slow. So astounded were those who first tried to cut iron meteorites with ordinary metal saws that one of the earliest practical results was the development of battleship armor plate composed of a commercial alloy called "meteor steel," which mimicked the composition of the iron meteorites.

Of course, a good deal of the difficulty of sectioning meteorites arises from the fact that those doing the cutting are trying hard not to waste valuable meteoritic material. Every precaution is taken to keep the amount of "sawdust" to a minimum, for such finely ground up and contaminated meteoritic material is of little scientific use. And, in addition, scientists must guard against heating meteorites to high temperatures because such heating destroys the delicate internal structure of the masses. If these two considerations (loss of material and overheating) were unimportant, even a large meteorite could easily be divided up by use of such high-powered oxyacetylene torches as are used to dissect huge obsolete battleships.

At the Institute of Meteoritics, a thin, water-cooled blade of soft iron is driven slowly back and forth by an electric motor. Carborundum grit in water suspension is fed evenly into the narrow cut over its entire length. This grit becomes imbedded in the lower edge of the soft iron blade, which then acts as a "many-toothed" metal saw. Several meteorites can be sectioned simultaneously by this multiblade saw. In the future, such newly developed methods as high-speed particle jet streams or ultrasonic devices may be used to section meteorites both rapidly and economically.

In the field of cosmic ray studies, particularly those concerned with the protection of space travelers from harmful radiation, meteoritics can be of help. The recovered meteorites have already come through those regions that would be crossed by even the farthest-ranging spaceships. Consequently, a great deal can be learned from the study of meteorites about the intensity of the cosmic radiation that the crews of such ships must face once they get outside the earth's protective air-shield.

The first study of this type was made in May, 1948, at the Institute for Nuclear Studies of the University of Chicago (now the Enrico Fermi Institute). Scientists made radioactivity tests on samples of the Norton County meteorite donated for this purpose by the Institute of Meteoritics and air-expressed to Chicago because of the intense interest in the radioactivity question. In October, 1949, English investigators ran similar tests at the Londonderry Laboratory for Radiochemistry, Durham, England, on samples of the freshly fallen Beddgelert, North Wales, meteorite discussed on pp. 69-70. The results of

The 6-blade meteorite gang-saw in the machine shop at the Institute
of Meteoritics.

these two pioneer studies were negative because the "Model-T" instruments available in 1948 and 1949 were not sensitive enough to detect the relatively low radioactivities present.

In 1955, however, scientists at Purdue University, using more refined counters, studied small nuggets of nickel-iron, also from the Norton meteorite. This time, the results of the radioactivity tests were positive. The investigators detected tritium (an isotope of hydrogen produced by cosmic-ray bombardment) in the samples. Furthermore, the *amount* of this rare isotope present indicated that the intensity of cosmic radiation outside the earth's atmosphere may be very much higher than had previously been thought possible. "Forewarned is forearmed," and from the standpoint of future astronauts, this is as practical a result as one could wish for!

In the relatively near future, men will certainly land on the surface of the moon. We know from radiometric studies that some degree of radioactivity is induced in meteorites by the full-intensity cosmic radiation to which they have been exposed during their motion through space. The nearly airless moon, like the meteorites, has also been exposed to very intense cosmic radiation for a long time. So those who are planning to land on our satellite are concerned about the radioactivities they will encounter when they begin their explorations of the lunar surface.

Suppose that extra-sensitive instruments were designed to pick up and measure the radioactivities. Suppose further that these instruments were mounted in a space-probe put in an orbit circling closely about the moon. Plans for such a project are now under way. What types and intensities of lunar radioactivities might such probe-mounted instruments record?

Until such a space-probe becomes available, earth-bound space-scientists are seeking at least a preliminary answer to this question. They are doing this by investigating the natural "probes" that have come to us from space—the meteorites.

Investigators have undertaken such studies very recently by employing a new radiometric method technically called *gamma-ray spectroscopy*. Work of this sort has been and is being done at the Los Alamos, New Mexico, Scientific Laboratory on scores of meteorite and tektite specimens loaned to the Laboratory by the Institute of Meteoritics. Some of the individual meteorite specimens tested weighed as much as 37 pounds, and are probably the largest single extra-terrestrial masses yet tested for cosmic ray-induced radioactivities.

Let us turn now to another important application of meteoritics. Any body in motion through the air or in space has a "striking power" of sorts. For some objects, this striking power, which is technically known as *ballistic potential,* is very weak, as in the case of silky milkweed-down drifting through the air. Hailstones have a good deal more striking power, as may have been painfully demonstrated on your own head. And, finally, such masses as falling meteorites (and especially those orbiting in space, unretarded by atmospheric resistance) have an extraordinarily formidable ballistic potential. This is because meteorites are not only tough and dense, as good projectiles must be, but are also moving at high velocities—particularly high if the meteorites come into the Solar System from interstellar space.

For this reason, the speeds of meteorites are very important to scientists responsible for rocket flights and for keeping satellites aloft over long periods of time. Clearly, these men must have as accurate information as possible on where and how fast meteoritic particles are moving, so as to chart the safest routes for spaceships, and to develop satisfactory means of protecting rockets and satellites against the effects of bombardment by the smaller meteorites. For these "small-fry" cosmic missiles are so numerous that many of them are sure to be encountered even in brief flights outside the earth's atmosphere.

Such information might also prove valuable in the future to the crews of spaceships on long flights into deep space. Such men may face the life or death problem of taking successful "evasive action" against giant meteorites that will seem like flying hills and mountains.

A strong parallelism exists between a meteorite fall and the re-entry of a nose-cone or data-capsule into the atmosphere. To a considerable extent, the difficult problems connected with the latter are being attacked at present through careful studies of meteorites. From the air-sculptured shapes of meteorites, their crustal flow patterns, and the thicknesses and types of fusion crusts they show, scientists are learning a great deal about certain factors connected with the re-entry problem. These factors include rate of vaporization, effects of extreme temperatures, and types of sculpturing to be expected as a result of encountering the resisting molecules of the atmosphere.

One of the most obvious applications of meteoritics in the future will grow out of the well-known fact that our earthly

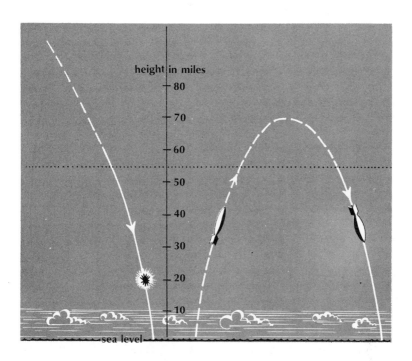

A. A METEORITE FALL   **B.** A V-2 RE-ENTRY

Relationship between (**A**) the trajectory of a falling meteorite, and
(**B**) the re-entry stage of a V-2 rocket. The solid lines indicate the
similar portions of the two trajectories.

resources of many strategic materials—especially metals like iron and nickel—are fast becoming exhausted. The population of the earth is increasing at a mad pace, and an end to metal-consuming wars is still not in sight. The need for such metals can only become more and more acute.

According to one of the currently favored explanations of the origin of the meteorites, the core-fragments of the parent meteorite-planet are solid masses of nickel-iron alloy—like the mass that blasted out the Canyon Diablo meteorite crater. If this meteorite-planet hypothesis finally wins general acceptance, the meteoriticist of the future is almost sure to be set the task of pin-pointing as exactly as possible the whereabouts in space and time of the most easily accessible cosmic nickel-iron lodes of this sort. Once he has given an answer, the space engineers will take over, and mining operations will be started on the unlimited sources of essential metals to be found in outer space.

Initially, no doubt, metal recoveries will be freighted back to earth in rocket-load lots. But as the need for iron and nickel increases on a metal-hungry earth, vast engineering projects may well be undertaken to "snare" the larger metal meteorites and equip them with rocket motors. This will be done so that by use of rocket power, the natural orbits of the meteorites can be changed into orbits bringing them back to earth. Unlike the natural, uncontrolled Canyon Diablo meteorite fall that vaporized what would have been a rich nickel-iron deposit, the rocket-controlled meteoritic "metal mines" will be eased down to earth all in one piece.

Reading of the possibility of sending out expeditions to find large iron meteorites in the depths of space may bring to your mind an image of the fearless mariners of old who sailed their stout ships over dangerous, often uncharted seas in search of the great whales. The rocket crews of day-after-tomorrow will no doubt be equally fearless and resourceful as they navigate the sea of space, intent on capturing the great "metal mines" of the future.

The experience gained in such space-mining ventures will then be carried over into expeditions to ensnare the larger stony-iron meteorites. These masses of iron and stone will offer less favorable mining possibilities, but they can be turned into rocket-propelled and guided de luxe space-cruisers. By this term, we do not mean that these natural space-ships will house all the luxuries of the ocean-liners advertised in the travel magazines. Rather, we see them as providing roomy, comfortable "underground" living quarters. Furthermore, their occupants will be adequately protected by great thicknesses of metal and rock from the injurious radiations of empty space, and the meteorites that make the term "empty space" something of a misnomer.

Initially, such worlds-in-miniature will be much sought after as laboratory sites where the more violent and dangerous of the many experimental tests which venturesome man will wish to conduct can be carried on without danger to the close-packed billions populating the then-crowded earth.

Later on, these meteorites-turned-into-space-ships may be used to explore the dangerous and faraway corners of the Solar

Oceanside Public Library

System, since the very substance of each massive meteoritic rocket-body will serve as an adequate and handy source of fuel supply.

When men have learned to live on such "homes away from home," it is quite possible that the larger of these modified meteorites, after their interiors have been opened up for occupancy by the inroads of the fuel-hungry rocket-motors, may be steered into neighborly orbits about old Mother Earth. Here, these "natural" satellites will assume the unexciting but necessary roles of the extra living quarters that by then will be so urgently needed to accommodate the mushrooming population of the world of the future.

People who live in these super-urban outliers of Mother Earth may take the same pride in their natural, if converted, homes as many former city dwellers now take in the old-fashioned sprawling farmhouses they have rebuilt and occupied. Perhaps one of your descendants will live in such a meteorite-orb, and occasionally point the finger of scorn at the more elegant but unpleasantly overcrowded artificial satellites preferred by those migrants from teeming earth who lack the true pioneering instinct. Who knows!

FOR FURTHER READING

IF YOU ARE especially interested in meteoritics, you already may have read some good books on general astronomy. There are many and most of them are not too advanced for the beginner. Unfortunately, these books devote but little space to meteoritics, the "Johnny-come-lately" of astronomy. Almost all of the writings on meteors and meteorites you will find largely profitable to read are in professional meteoritical publications. A selected list of such publications, containing much or at least a worthwhile amount of material you will now be able to understand, is given below. Your chief difficulty in using this list will be in finding some of the more important items in the holdings of your public library, unless it is a large and well-stocked one. Your librarian, however, may be able to help you get the item from some other library—perhaps from that of a nearby university or college.

METEORIC ASTRONOMY

MEBANE, A. D. "The Canadian Fireball Procession of 1913, February 9," *Meteoritics,* Vol. 1, No. 4 (1956), pp. 405-421. Eyewitness accounts of the most famous fireball procession on record.

OLIVIER, C. P. *Meteors,* Williams and Wilkins, Baltimore, 1925. An exhaustive survey of work done by visual meteor-observers.

SCHIAPARELLI, G. V. *Shooting Stars,* a translation by C. C. Wylie and J. R. Naiden, published in the *Proceedings, Iowa Academy of Science,* Vol. 50 (1943), pp. 48-153. A pioneer treatise, dated 1867, which is basic to later work in this field.

WHIPPLE, F. L. "Photographic Meteor Studies, I," *Proceedings, American Philosophical Society,* Vol. 79, No. 4 (1938), pp. 499-548. Fundamental paper on the subject. Of the six meteors analyzed, five followed elliptical orbits and one, a strongly hyperbolic orbit.

METEORITES

FARRINGTON, O. C. "A Catalogue of the Meteorites of North America to January 1, 1909," *Memoirs, National Academy of Sciences,* Vol. 13 (1915). Contains fascinating accounts of the phenomena connected with meteorite falls, interspersed with lengthy technical chemical and microscopic studies of meteorites.

FARRINGTON, O. C. *Meteorites* [published by the author], Chicago, 1915. The classic American work on meteorites. The first half of the book is popular; the last half is technical.

HEY, M. H. and PRIOR, G. T. *Catalogue of Meteorites,* William Clowes & Sons, London, 1953. An exhaustive catalog of all recognized and also, unfortunately, of many doubtful meteorite falls and finds, from the beginning of the historical record up to December 1952.

LAPAZ, LINCOLN. "The Achondritic Shower of February 18, 1948," *Publications, Astronomical Society of the Pacific,* Vol. 61 (1949), pp. 63-73.

LAPAZ, LINCOLN. "The Effects of Meteorites upon the Earth," *Advances in Geophysics,* Vol. 4, edited by H. E. Landsberg, Academic Press, New York, 1958, pp. 217-350. A monograph covering such topics as meteorite hits upon buildings and people, meteorite detectors, and the nature and age of meteorite craters.

LEONARD, F. C. "The Furnas County, Kansas, Achondritic Fall (1000,400)," *Contributions, Meteoritical Society,* Vol. 4 (1948), pp. 138-141. This paper and the eighth item, above, discuss the phenomena of the fall of the largest aerolite so far recovered anywhere in the world.

MERRILL, G. P. "The Story of Meteorites," *Minerals from Earth and Sky,* Vol. 3, Part I, Smithsonian Scientific Series, 1929, pp. 1-163. A chiefly popular survey of the subject by a master meteoriticist.

PERRY, S. H. *The Metallography of Meteoric* [meteoritic] *Iron,* U. S. National Museum Bulletin No. 184 (1944). A summary of knowledge on the subject, supplemented by exceptionally fine photographs of etched meteorite sections.

SWINDEL, G. W., JR., and JONES, WALTER B. "The Sylacauga, Talladega County, Alabama, Aerolite: A Recent Meteoritic Fall that Injured a Human Being," *Meteoritics,* Vol. 1, No. 2 (1954), pp. 125-132.

WHITE, C. S. and BENSON, OTIS O. (editors) *Physics and Medicine of the Upper Atmosphere,* University of New Mexico Press, Albuquerque, 1952. See Chapter X, "Meteoritic Phenomena and Meteorites," by F. L. Whipple, pp. 137-170; and Chapter XIX, "Meteoroids, Meteorites, and Hyperbolic Meteoritic Velocities," by Lincoln LaPaz, pp. 352-393. Modern views on the meteorite velocity controversy.

METEORITE CRATERS

LAPAZ, LINCOLN. "The Craters on the Moon," *Scientific American,* Vol. 181, No. 4 (1949), pp. 2-3. A popular exposition of the Bénard-Wasiutynski theory of the origin of the ordinary (non-rayed) craters on the moon.

SPENCER, L. J. "Meteorite Craters as Topographical Features on the Earth's Surface," *Geographical Journal,* Vol. 81 (1933), pp. 227-248. The classic paper on terrestrial meteorite craters.

METEORITIC DUST

BUDDHUE, J. D. *Meteoritic Dust,* The University of New Mexico Press, Albuquerque, 1950. An account of the various techniques used in collecting and studying meteoritic dust; and also of the conclusions drawn from the study of such dust.

INDEX

White, C. S., 179
Widmanstätten pattern, 120, 121, 122, 158
Whipple, F. L., 177, 179
Willamette iron, 36, 128, 129
Wold Cottage meteorite, 156
Wolf Creek crater, 52, 53, 65, 75, 133

Y

Yale University, 41
young people and meteoritics, 23, 24, 28, 34, 39, 90, 98, 99, 116, *see also* reports, eyewitness

Z

Zhovtnevy Hutor fall, 82

Oceanside Public Library